'I didn't misu[nde]

Luke spoke c[alm]

'There was no [...]
you flaunted yo[...]
I was curious [...] he
brought your na[me ... w]hen we started looking for a new programme manager.'

'What a shock for you when I accepted the
position,' Maria snapped.

Luke laughed. 'But I wanted it to happen.
Haven't you realised that I have plans for
you?'

Dear Reader

Spring is just around the corner; for some this new season may bring a dose of 'spring-fever'—perhaps starting a new diet, thinking about a holiday, or cleaning your house from top to bottom. Others will welcome the longer, lighter days and the first flowers. Whatever your mood, this month Mills & Boon has a great selection of bright, fresh romances, with tempting backgrounds: Greece, Africa, Taiwan and the spectacular Winter Carnival in Venice to name but a few . . . and we're planning plenty more in the year to come!

The Editor

Jayne Bauling was born in England and grew up in South Africa. She always wrote but was too shy to show anyone until the publication of some poems in her teens gave her the confidence to attempt the romances she wanted to concentrate on, the first published being written while attending business college. Her home is just outside Johannesburg, a town house ruled by a sealpoint called Ranee. Travel is a major passion; at home it's family, friends, music, swimming, reading and patio gardening.

RANSACKED
HEART

BY
JAYNE BAULING

MILLS & BOON LIMITED
ETON HOUSE   18–24 PARADISE ROAD
RICHMOND   SURREY   TW9 1SR

First published in Great Britain 1993 by Mills & Boon Limited

© Jayne Bauling 1993

Australian copyright 1993 Philippine copyright 1993 This edition 1993

ISBN 0 263 77937 8

Set in 10 on 11 pt Linotron Times 01-9303-55547

Typeset in Great Britain by Centracet, Cambridge Made and printed in Great Britain

CHAPTER ONE

'Can you believe it, Maria? The two of us together again!'

Maria McFadden turned sparkling eyes on the fair man who called himself Florian Jones.

'You might not be sounding quite so enthusiastic this time next week,' she cautioned him laughingly.

'I won't let you rain on my parade,' he retorted. 'We were always good together.'

The tiny inner *frisson* of unease that silenced her laughter was unexpected, and she hesitated before responding, examining the message of her senses and dismissing it. Somehow Florian's words must have summoned the memory of that first time they had worked together, long years ago, and that sensation of a shadow falling on her had come from the past.

Her stilted smile reappeared, placing a dent at one corner of her mouth, but she waited a few seconds longer, making sure that the ghost had retreated again. This was Taiwan. Her present and her foreseeable future lay here, and they looked good.

Taipei itself looked beautiful from the high balcony on which she and Florian stood, by night a glittering bowl from which the hum and roar of its mind-numbing traffic rose to compete with the sounds of the party going on in the large room behind them.

'But this time I'll be your boss. The job may go under different titles on different stations around the world, but essentially that's what I'll be from Monday on, even if you do earn more than me.' No longer

haunted, Maria offered the eventual reminder mischievously, and Florian grinned.

'In a sense,' he allowed carelessly.

'Oh, you're the star,' she conceded mockingly, currently in a mood to indulge his ego. 'But not tonight,
my friend.'

'No, it's your night,' Florian agreed generously.

'And as the party is for me, let's get back to it,' she
suggested happily. 'It was sweet of Giles to think of it.'

'The real boss, when you remember that commercial
radio is about money,' he emphasised. 'And sweetness
doesn't have much to do with it, my love. You're an
important lady, now that we're getting so competitive.
Someone told me that even the ultimate big boss
himself was planning to look in this evening—probably
to inspect your body and soul, now that he owns them.'

'You're exaggerating as usual. I never committed
those when I signed my contract.'

'Nevertheless, we're talking ownership here,' Florian
insisted as they turned towards the open door. 'He
owns us, the studios from which we broadcast and the
building they're in, although by now he must have
recovered whatever his original investment was several
times over. You have to hand it to the man. He's only
thirty-four, and he's done the same thing all over the
Far East, taking over struggling and usually amateur or
pirate radio stations like this one once was, and putting
in people like me who pull commercial sponsorship
because we draw listeners. His other interests are all
sound-orientated too; he owns recording studios all
over the region, for instance—that sort of thing, with
the emphasis on sound as a commodity. Big bucks,
darling. I guess we could call him a sound
entrepreneur.'

'That's what radio is all about—sound.'

Maria paused in the doorway, surveying her new

colleagues and their partners, a handful of them local people but mainly men and women from all over the English-speaking world, because radio people had a gypsy tendency to move on every few years. You met up again every so often, as she and Florian had done now. The Taipei job was only unusual in that it would be a new experience to work in a country where English was not the official language, but the presence of a large population of Westerners, the bulk of them American, ensured high listenership figures even with the competition provided by the existence of other English-language stations.

Maria had loved radio with a passion from early childhood, her faith in its power to survive unimpaired through all the years when television threatened to make it obsolete, and justified now that it was enjoying an upsurge in popularity in so many countries, thriving new stations almost daily news at present.

'He's here,' Florian observed from just behind her.

A question died unspoken as she saw him. Her heart stopped, and when it beat again the shadow had returned, if shadows had weight, because this one oppressed her, but only momentarily. Then she was able to take the mental step that brought her out into the light again.

Her eyes blazed.

Once he had possessed the power to disturb her, but no longer. Now there was only hatred left.

The extent of her fury disconcerted her fleetingly, fully alive and as fulminatingly intense as ever, despite all the years that had gone by since she had last felt like this.

'That's Luke Scott, Florian!' she said sharply.

'Sure, didn't Giles ever mention him?' Florian was surprised.

Maria's tenderly passionate mouth tightened. Did

Florian think she would be here if the name had occurred in the almost six months of correspondence between her and Giles? But perhaps he did. Florian was renowned for many things, but sensitivity wasn't among them.

'No, and neither did you,' she said tautly, her party mood a distant memory. 'Florian, don't you remember? That—that man had me fired from that very first job, the one you organised for me back in South Africa when I left school!'

'Hell, I haven't thought about that station in years.' Florian laughed and shrugged. 'There are always so many firings in radio that it hardly seems a big deal any more.'

'It was a big deal to me at the time,' Maria snapped, her tolerance of his perpetual self-absorption vanished along with her brilliant mood.

'Oh, come on!' he began to protest easily.

'Don't you remember the way he did it?' Maria's eyes were pure topaz. 'It was after that weekend gig in Zimbabwe—but I seem to remember that you took two weeks' leave immediately after that, so perhaps you never knew. It wasn't the usual rationalisation procedure, believe me! I arrived at work on the Monday and was handed a cheque and my personal belongings at the desk in the foyer and was then escorted out by Security. It took me a week to get myself together again, and by the time you got back from leave I'd left Johannesburg because there weren't any jobs for me there. The subject never came up when our paths crossed in Sydney three years ago, did it? God, Florian! And my father——'

'Well, as you say, a rationalisation process was under way. There were loads of retrenchments,' Florian reminded her indifferently as she broke off, choking on complex, raging emotion. 'If you remember, Luke

Scott was with us for six months as a favour to the station's director-general, who was a friend of his, because our listenership figures were dropping and we were losing advertising. He had *carte blanche* as long as he revived our fortunes—luckily he knew I was the station's biggest asset. You were just a junior, a sort of Girl Friday with no qualifications, hoping to learn the ropes.'

'I needed that job. It was paying for my Communications course.'

'Does it matter now? You made it in radio without it,' Florian pointed out carelessly.

Maria shook her head angrily, aware of the futility of trying to explain the dilemma she had faced all those years ago to a man whose self-centredness precluded his ever having had to make a choice between his own interests and someone else's.

Her eyes had remained on the tall, casually dressed man at the other side of the room, noting that little had changed in six years. He still held himself with the easy confidence she remembered, his dark head carried at an unconsciously arrogant angle, and he still had that polish to him, the patina of success.

He had been talking to a tall girl with white-blonde hair, but suddenly he turned his head slightly and looked straight at Maria, and every muscle in her body clenched in furious, shocked resistance. Reason said he couldn't possibly have any recollection of a nineteen-year-old nobody he had once caused to be dismissed from her first job, but the knowledge of her bones was stronger.

Luke Scott remembered her.

'I thought he came to us from Hong Kong that time? But he's English originally, isn't he?' she prompted Florian, as if she could alter the truth by uncovering an error.

'Hong Kong is where he's based. I told you, he has interests all over this part of the world. We don't usually get this much hands-on attention from him, but I suspect that Cavell Fielding has something to do with his presence as he's lending us her talents for the launch of our new look—or sound, I should say. The blonde. She's his Hong Kong operation's media liaison chief. Well, that's her official, public position. Unofficially and privately——'

'Ah, Maria!' Giles Estwick, the Englishman who handled the station's financial affairs and commercial deals, had appeared at her side. 'I was going to give the two of you a few more minutes out there, but if you've exhausted old times you can come and meet Luke Scott.'

'I must find Nicky,' said Florian, and drifted away.

A dangerous sparkle of anticipation in her eyes, Maria drew her shoulders back and walked across the room with her host at her side. There were women present who were more beautiful than she was, notably the blonde beside Luke Scott and Nicky Kai, the world-famous Taiwanese ex-model, but the languid sway of Maria's hips above long slim legs drew attention, as did her unusual colouring, an exotic combination of olive-toned skin, streaky brown and blonde hair and eyes that could be anything from copper to amber, depending on her mood.

She was aware of Luke Scott watching her, but heedless of anyone else. Dark grey eyes, Celtic eyes, were ironic, as was his smile as Giles made the introductions, including Cavell Fielding, and Maria returned it with her own piquantly imperfect smile.

'But we've met before, haven't we, Mr Scott?'

She was driven by a need to get in first, her mood openly aggressive.

'Of course.' He was urbane, and very slightly taunting. 'Although I don't recall that we ever actually spoke to each other.'

Maria laughed, a lovely liquid sound, but it required an effort of will to lift her hand and place it in his outstretched one, and resentment surged as his fingers closed round it briefly and were removed.

Shaking hands with the enemy. The distaste she experienced was so intense that she felt dizzy for several seconds.

'I was too much in awe of you to utter in those days,' she confessed, lightly dismissive and matching the subtle mockery of his tone.

It was a palatable version of the truth, and one she had spent years working at believing. Six years ago she had been tongue-tied in his presence, and terrified by the strength of her reaction to him, her fear manifesting itself physically, stopping the breath in her throat, tensing her muscles and making her nerves leap every time he moved or spoke to anyone, and the rare occasions on which his glance had strayed idly in her direction, it had actually hurt her. It had been as if he came from another, alien world, beyond her experience or comprehension, a glamorous, glittering man who made her think of diamonds, so hard and sharp were the edges of his personality.

'This was in South Africa about—what?—six years ago,' he told Giles and Cavell. 'Your first job, wasn't it, Maria?'

'It didn't last long,' she said drily. 'Yes, Florian Jones had organised it for me.'

'And since then the two of you have got together in Australia once, and now again in Taiwan, of course.'

The contempt, or criticism, was probably hidden from the others, but Maria was acutely aware of it, and incensed.

'I got him the Sydney job,' she vouchsafed with delicate emphasis.

'And since Sydney she's been in Wellington, gaining experience as a programme manager.' Giles was understandably intent on selling her appointment to their real boss.

'So Taipei isn't even a promotion.' Luke sketched a smile, his tone still laden with mockery.

'Just a change,' Maria asserted blithely, hating him—*hating* him.

'And a challenge? Cavell is co-ordinating our media campaign, and she'll want to discuss it with you—won't you?' The quick smile he directed at Cavell was utterly different from the one Maria had just received. 'But right now, if you don't mind, Giles, I think Cavell should meet Penny Seu Chen so that they can sort out Maria's schedule for the next few days, as I doubt if Maria has had time to familiarise herself with it yet. Penny is here, isn't she?'

It was so skilfully effected that Giles and Cavell were metres away before Maria realised what was happening. She looked at Luke and he looked back at her, a stretched quality to the silence between them.

Dear God, why should she still find him so disturbing after all he had done to her?

The deep grey eyes were shadowed, but she didn't miss the glitter in their depths as they skimmed her vivid party make-up and party clothes, brief ivory skirt revealing the length of her legs, the matching top moulded to proud breasts, the emerald of the silky, fringed shawl tied tightly about her waist a bright splash of colour between the two.

'And what are you planning to do about Nicky Kai?' he asked her very softly.

'I gave up worrying about Florian's women years ago,' she responded automatically, her cynicism where

Florian's personal affairs were concerned so complete it had almost become tolerance. 'Not that I was aware that there was a problem there. Mr Scott——'

'Then maybe you should start again,' he cut her short. 'Nicky honed her fighting skills in the toughest business in the world, modelling in Paris and New York, and she's not ready to move on yet.'

It distracted Maria from the attack she had intended to launch.

'I'm not here to steal Florian from Nicky.' It was scathing.

He shrugged indifferently, but contempt lurked in his eyes.

'Then perhaps you don't mind sharing, the way you once shared him with the little South African girl who was having such a miserable pregnancy when I was there trying to breathe some life into that Johannesburg radio station six years ago.'

Stunned, Maria drew a sharp little breath. Then her face hardened.

'Is that why I lost my job?'

'You lost your job because the station was losing money and you were superfluous.' It was brutal, devoid of apology. 'There was no discipline, and too many niches had been conveniently created for too many friends, lovers and other attachments. You were a financial drain.'

She laughed sceptically. 'And I suppose you're going to tell me that the manner in which I was dismissed was standard procedure?'

'Desperate situations require desperate remedies. But why is it still important? Parting you from Jones that time doesn't seem to have curtailed your ongoing little adventure—not that I thought it would.'

'That job was the adventure,' she remembered, but

he had deprived her of so much more than just adventure.

'Somehow I suspect that emotion is clouding your memory of that period,' Luke returned incisively. 'Jones was very much part of the adventure. Wherever he was, there you would be, hanging around even when you weren't on duty——'

'I was learning about radio!' Maria cut in furiously.

'You even tagged along to that concert in Harare when he was one of the compères,' Luke recalled.

Maria's eyes glowed amber, and hostility held her rigid outwardly. Inside, she was shaking with rage.

'And that's what it was all about, wasn't it? The way I was dismissed? It had nothing to do with whether I was redundant or not. You'd passed judgement on my morals and decided to punish me for something you could only have had the vaguest idea about. I'd just like to know from what sort of position you assumed the right to do so, Mr Scott. Have you led such a pure life yourself?' Smouldering now, her eyes strayed significantly in Cavell Fielding's direction.

Disgust made his lip curl.

'Probably not so pure, but at least I've stayed clear of triangles,' he retorted flatly.

'Lucky you!' she mocked.

'Luck hasn't come into it,' he contradicted her arrogantly. 'Just good judgement.'

Her laughter was taunting. 'I didn't see much evidence of it when you were dealing with me!'

'No, I didn't misjudge you, Maria. There was no chance of my doing so, the way you were flaunting your relationship with Jones—and you haven't learned a thing since then,' Luke added contemptuously. 'You got together again in Sydney a few years ago, I'm told, and here you are a third time. I didn't think you'd be that stupid, but I was curious enough to consent when

Jones brought your name up with Giles Estwick when we started thinking about looking for a new programme manager six months ago.'

'What a shock for you when I accepted the position,' Maria snapped. 'What are you going to do now? The contract I signed legally binds the station as much as it does me. I suppose you weren't around and you realised too late what had happened.'

He laughed. 'But I wanted it to happen. I have plans for you, Miss Maria McFadden. Haven't you realised yet?'

She didn't want to understand him, but heated recognition rippled through her as she stared at his mouth, as unwillingly fascinated by its sensual curve as she had been six years ago, when all her breathlessly adored heroes had suddenly become prosaic and petty with the advent of the man from Hong Kong.

'What do you want?' It wasn't the question she had meant to ask.

Instead of answering it, he gave her an ironically considering look. 'You've got a lot more to say for yourself these days, haven't you?'

She flung him a savage little smile. 'Does remembering how awed I was give you a thrill? Was it an affirmation of your power? I was nineteen—of course I was in awe of you. I'd never met anyone like you, and the fact that there was a rumour that you were newly in mourning for your father just added to the mystique, because I was young enough to find tragedy romantic.'

For a time she had even innocently believed that Luke's father's recent death had been responsible for the anger she had sensed in him, until she gradually grew aware that it was something personal, directed at her, his dealings with most of the station's personnel characterised by charm, his impatience with any inadequacies purely professional.

'Hardly in mourning,' Luke asserted distastefully, his features hard with something akin to rejection. 'The man had died and I was getting on with my life.'

'Oh, yes, I've realised since that you weren't like the rest of us ordinary human beings who are unfortunate enough to be troubled by feelings like grief and guilt.' It was bitterly resentful, her hatred burning high as she remembered the months running into years that it had taken for her to convince herself that the guilt she had felt after her own father's death was a self-destructive trap and just one more wrong done to her by Luke Scott. 'But I was an innocent in those days. There you were, come to save our pathetic little radio station, and just about the first thing you did was scoop that concert in Harare, and at the height of the cultural boycott, because you'd emphasised our independent nature. We were actually presenting it in conjunction with that soft-drinks company, our three best DJs the compères.'

'And you came along for the ride?'

'Since Florian could hardly have taken his wife with him when she was so sick all the time.'

'I understand that he's still married to her?'

A shadow crossed Maria's face. 'Yes.'

Luke's mouth curved derisively. 'It didn't bother you six years ago, so why should it now? Nicky Kai doesn't mind.'

She flung up her head, rage blazing in her eyes. 'You seriously believe it, don't you? That I was having an affair with Florian? And that I want to get together with him again now?'

'Not forgetting your reunion in Sydney.' He shrugged expressively. 'Why not, if the two of you are so good together? You were congratulating yourselves on the fact earlier, I know.'

It took her a moment or two to realise what he was referring to and remember Florian's words out on the balcony.

'Eavesdropping!' she accused him caustically.

There was something cruel about his smile now. 'Don't worry—any more intimate reminiscences escaped me, as I discovered a strong disinclination to hear the sordid details of your relationship.'

'Then why raise the subject now?' Maria countered. 'You can't have any real scruples about our supposed affair or we wouldn't be working for you, so I can only assume that you're making this personal attack for the sheer hell of it, because you once got a kick out of disapproving of me—despising me—and you're trying to recapture the thrill of it all.'

The grey eyes glittered. 'You and Florian Jones are employed because you're both good at what you do——'

'Thank you,' she inserted tartly. 'As it happens, that's what Flo was referring to when you overheard us, Mr Scott—our professional relationship. So if you don't mind, let's keep this conversation equally professional, please.'

'When what's between us is so personal?'

The tone was silkily challenging, and Maria's heart jumped in startled recognition before instinctive denial asserted itself.

'There's nothing personal between us.'

'You owe me, Maria,' Luke added intently.

'I owe you nothing!' she retorted tempestuously. 'If anything, the reverse is true. You owe me, Mr Scott, except that nothing can ever compensate for what you stole from me six years ago.'

'I didn't steal anything from you, and what you lost, you had no right to in the first place.' He was remorseless, but his voice had dropped to a silken taunt as he went on, 'But tell me what you think it is I owe you, Maria. I'm interested to hear.'

'You've got nothing I want.' Maria was scornful.

His smile was blistering. 'You want.'

'Other than this job,' she added challengingly, some perverse part of her almost wishing he would attempt to deprive her of it so that she would have something real, present and immediate to fight him for.

'Which you have. This time I'm not letting you off so lightly—which is what I was actually doing when I had you dismissed from that other one,' he stated outrageously.

'Hardly!'

'I could have destroyed you six years ago,' he continued.

'And didn't you just do your best?' Bitterness rose. 'My job——'

'I'm not talking about your dismissal or even the fact that it parted you from Jones, and I think you know it.' The claim was confident. 'I'm talking about the way things were between us. As I say, I could have destroyed you, or so I thought at the time, but you've turned out to be a lot tougher than I had imagined. . . not vulnerable or confused at all. This time I don't have to restrain myself; I don't have to be merciful. I know what you are and that you can cope.'

'With what? Being destroyed by you?' she quipped wildly.

'Weren't you listening? I've realised that you neither required nor merited consideration. Nor do you now, and this time you won't get it.' Luke paused deliberately, his eyes holding hers. 'You're not stupid and you're not innocent, Maria. You knew what it was all about six years ago—what was happening.'

It was as if she was bound by silken cords, soft yet irresistibly strong. Maria couldn't move her head or even lower her eyes, and time had slipped. She was nineteen and choked by the immensity of her reaction to this man, unable to breathe or stir, and panicked by the conviction that Luke was seeing into her secret self, invading, bent on vandalising and stealing. Every time he looked her way, that frightening compulsion went sweeping through her, the urge to let him look, let him absorb her until nothing was left and she no longer existed as a separate, individual entity. She was a confident, outgoing girl who usually interacted quite happily with people of either sex and any age, but she was reduced to silence in Luke Scott's presence, so deeply did he disturb her.

A trick of time. She was twenty-five, her hormones under control, her identity secure and her spirit her own, safe from thieves. She showed Luke her smile.

'Weren't *you* listening to me earlier? Yes, I know what was happening. You were a romantic figure, come to restore our fortunes. The awe I felt was probably the first phase of hero-worship—the sort of thing some people call a crush. Oh, it was uncomfortable.' She gestured mockingly. 'And confusing, since I never reached the stage of identifying my affliction. Maybe I do owe you something after all. If you hadn't made me hate you, it might have gone on for months.'

'Ah, hatred.' Luke was smoothly reflective. 'Much more comfortable.'

'And it lasts.' Maria looked straight at him with hard eyes. 'I still hate you, Mr Scott.'

'Then call me Luke, as there's a certain intimacy to hatred. It's a very personal thing,' he taunted. 'And there you were, insisting that there's nothing personal between us.'

'You must have hated me too!' she flared, caught, and angry enough to show her resentment, past and present. 'All right, your claim that I was superfluous is

probably valid, so why wasn't I made redundant in the
usual way? Let go, as the euphemism has it? There'd
have been no comebacks for the station. I didn't belong
to a union, I didn't know anything about my rights
then, and I know now that I didn't have any in that
particular case. . . But you actively made my dismissal
a punishment.'

'You must have thought you merited punishment,
for the idea to have occurred to you at all.'

'The way I was dismissed ensured that it occurred to
me,' Maria asserted tightly. 'Except that I had no idea
what I was being punished for.'

'Because you felt no guilt about what you were
doing?' Luke probed inimically.

'My supposed affair with Florian?' Maria just managed to keep her voice low. 'Even if you hadn't been
way out there, you had no right to make something
from my personal life the grounds for dismissal.'

'The method of your dismissal,' he corrected her.
'You were due to lose that job anyway.'

'You admit it, then? That it was personal?'

'We've just been agreeing that what's between us is
personal, haven't we?'

'Only in the most negative sense, and only then, not
now.' Maria was defiant.

Luke laughed with genuine amusement, but something hard and unyielding still lay behind the surface
gleam in his eyes.

'More than ever now. As I say, you owe me something, and if you're determined to go on pretending
you don't know that, I'll be delighted to tell you what
it is some time soon, but not right now. We're attracting too much attention. In fact——' his upper lip curled
fastidiously as he paused thoughtfully '—in fact, if we
didn't have our professional connection to serve as
camouflage, I don't think I'd care to be seen with you.

It's just a pity we don't live in the era when a man could set his mistress up somewhere and know she'd be there waiting for him whenever he felt the urge to see her, but was never, ever seen with her in public.'

Immobile, barely breathing, Maria didn't speak for several seconds. Then she said tightly, 'I'm not your mistress.'

'No, but you're going to be.'

This time her silence was longer. She had known, hadn't she? Oh, yes, she had recognised the sexual awareness that was the dark other side of Luke's hostility—and had tried to ignore it, but it was impossible to go on pretending it didn't exist now that the preliminary skirmishing was over and he was referring to it openly.

Apprehension was a physical pang, the ensuing denial a wash of red-hot feeling. Never!

The thought was frantic as she dragged a desperate breath into her lungs. She hated Luke Scott, so——

Just say no.

Maria suppressed rising panic that was fatally laced with hysteria. Where had that stupid slogan come from, the facile answer of those who thought there were easy solutions to all the world's problems? Nothing was that simple.

The way he was looking at her——

'When I'm so cheap and nasty?' she jeered, a soft acknowledgement of the contempt with which he was regarding her.

'Cheap,' he granted her ruthlessly, and smiled as she glanced in the direction of Florian, who was now dancing energetically with the exotically lovely Nicky Kai. 'No, Jones won't be rescuing you, even supposing Nicky is into sharing. He can name his price and I'll pay it because he's a brilliant jock, but that's it and he knows it.'

In a happier moment, Maria might have laughed at
the idea of Florian troubling to rescue anyone from
anything.

'I don't need rescuing.' She lifted her chin. 'No one
has mistresses any more.'

'I know, but what other word is there? We'd both
balk at "lover". People just get married or live
together,' Luke went on relentlessly. 'But those don't
apply to us as they imply a sharing that's total, and
there's only one area of my life that I can bring myself
to share with you.'

The insult enraged her.

'Unfortunately there isn't a single square inch of my
life I want to share with you,' she told him levelly, the
mad, febrile fluttering of her heart a private weakness.

'This time I'm not considering you,' Luke returned
callously, and produced a brilliant smile. 'Come, let
me introduce you to people. Who haven't you met
yet?'

As they moved around the room, Luke introducing
her to the people with whom she would be working,
Maria struggled to put his threats out of her mind and
minimise her own reaction to him, both six years ago
and now. Whatever she had felt at nineteen, hatred
was all that was left now, and hatred ought to impart
strength. Luke Scott meant nothing to her; he couldn't
do anything to her if she refused to let him.

But she remained disturbed, acutely aware of him at
her side and only grateful that he despised her too
much to allow himself to be seen touching her in
public.

Even the convention of a hand at her elbow would
have been intolerable. That was how much she hated
him.

She glanced at him, almost hopefully, but the impact
of his virility and arrogance remained undiminished,

and her fingers curled into her palms, painted nails slicing the soft skin. He was quite simply devastating, a combination of grace and power, allied to the pride implicit in strong, superb facial bones over which dark coppery skin was stretched tautly. He was clean-shaven, although a faint darkness marked his jaw at this hour; inevitable with his colouring, she knew, her eyes moving upwards to his jet-black hair and then—a betrayal of herself—down to where the open neck of his shirt provided tantalising glimpses of subtly gleaming flesh shadowed by softly curling dark hair, all so emphatically masculine.

It was a dangerous moment, fascination obliterating resentment, but when Luke suddenly turned his eyes her way again, the contempt Maria saw in them restored hatred.

CHAPTER TWO

'CAN we give you a lift?'

Maria flung Luke Scott a hostile look as he and Cavell Fielding appeared just as she was taking her leave of Giles and Ursula Estwick, with Florian and Nicky on either side of her.

'I'm going home with Florian and Nicky, thanks.'

It was deliberately dismissive, but a scorching anger rose in response to the searingly contemptuous look he gave her.

'We've managed to wangle her an apartment just a floor below Nicky and me,' Florian volunteered cheerfully. 'Well, it was Nicky's influence really, I have to admit. It takes Taipei's most famous daughter to buck our letting agent's system of waiting lists like that.'

'It sounds like a convenient arrangement,' Luke commented urbanely, and Maria saw his lip curl sardonically, as if everything he believed of her had just been confirmed.

What did he think they were going to do? Toss a coin to determine on which floor Florian spent the night?

'Cosy,' she offered flippantly with a defiantly challenging smile.

'Obviously,' he drawled.

Maria met Cavell's watchful sapphire eyes and a furious resentment gripped her, felt on Cavell's behalf almost as much as her own, because Luke couldn't have spoken to her as he had earlier, openly stating that he intended to make her his mistress, if he had

had any real regard for Cavell, or women in general,
for that matter.

'See you tomorrow, then, Cavell,' she confirmed an
arrangement they had made during the course of the
evening, ignoring Luke now but still acutely conscious
of his attention as she thanked the Estwicks again and
departed with Florian and Nicky.

'Luke Scott doesn't like you any better yet, Flo,'
Nicky commented amusedly when they were in a taxi.

'I'm a woman's man,' Florian returned complacently
as their driver eased his slow way out of one of the
traffic jams that were a major problem in Taipei.
'Other men can resent that.'

Maria shook her head, her smile a little cynical.

'You don't think his dislike might be a little more
personal than that?' she wondered casually.

'As gorgeous as she is, I don't go for women like
Cavell Fielding.' Typically, Florian laughed, natural
vanity making him misunderstand her. 'Although I
suppose he might suspect her of fancying me! I have to
say this, though—whatever it is, he's never let it
become a big issue. He ignores me when he can and I
co-operate by keeping out of his way, because I like
the job. He's never allowed his dislike, personal or
otherwise, to influence his professional judgement in
any way. He knows I'm the best jock he's got here.
But generally it's been unnecessary for us to have much
contact. As I told you earlier, he spends most of his
time in Hong Kong, where his major interests are.'

It was just a pity that Luke hadn't decided to ignore
her as well, Maria reflected wryly. The policy he
applied to Florian would have suited her perfectly.

As it was, the most she could hope for was his speedy
return to Hong Kong, but for now she supposed she
would just have to endure a certain amount of contact,

as he had warned her earlier at the party just before leaving her with Cavell Fielding and Penny Seu Chen.

'I plan to be around over the next few weeks while we get this new image launched, and we expect you to be very visible. Obviously we haven't gone for wholesale personnel changes, so you're the hook on which we're hanging the idea, a new programme manager whose own image is the station's—young, smart, sophisticated and committed to the music. Taiwan is one of the most Westernised countries in this region, and our last few surveys have shown that we're attracting an extensive local listenership now, covering an age-group ranging from mid-teens to late thirties, so we want to ditch a lingering perception that we exist solely for the benefit of non-nationals. Giles Estwick will have discussed it with you, and you'll have ideas of your own. Cavell will want to hear what they are, as well as some appropriate biographical details for Press releases, as she's handling the publicity angle for us. She's the best there is, so consult her if there's anything you're unsure of on that side.'

'But only on that side?' Maria had prompted derisively.

Luke's smile was equally mocking. 'Obviously we understand each other perfectly already.'

'I understand you,' she corrected him sharply. 'I should. Rats aren't exactly rare.'

'Highly intelligent, though,' Luke retorted dismissively, apparently uperturbed, but hostility still glinted in his eyes.

'Every rule has its exception,' she snapped.

She could work with Cavell, Maria had decided by the next afternoon. Along with a Chinese freelance photographer, Cavell had called for her that morning and whisked her round some of Taipei's famous landmarks, the all-marble Chiang Kai-Shek Memorial, a

colourful Buddhist temple, and the Grand Hotel with
its magnificent Chinese architecture, pausing only long
enough at each for the young man to take the photos
that would help introduce Maria to the Taipei public,
before escorting her back to the apartment and approv-
ing the outfit she planned to wear to the dinner the
radio station was hosting for the rest of the local media
that night.

'You'd better have the afternoon to yourself as I
imagine the heat and humidity must be hitting you,'
she decided, preparing to depart. 'We'll see you
tonight.'

'Will everyone be attending?' asked Maria.

'Except for whoever's on duty. It's expected,' Cavell
added drily.

'Mr Scott?'

'Of course. He's taking a personal interest in this.'

Personal. The word disturbed Maria for a while
afterwards, although Cavell probably hadn't given it
any real thought, since she appeared so untroubled,
her manner calmly confident and still strictly
professional.

Maria was checking her public face, glittering tawny
colour smudged lightly over her eyelids, darkening at
the outer corners, lips defined with vivid colour, when
the doorbell rang that evening, and she went to open
it, expecting Nicky Kai, who had telephoned during
the afternoon to suggest that the three of them share a
taxi again tonight.

Surprise made her catch a breath, but it was the
swiftly ensuing resentment that held it locked in her
lungs for seconds after she should have expelled it as
she stared questioningly at Luke Scott, casually elegant
in a beautifully made lightweight jacket worn over a
pale shirt and obviously expensive trousers with a
discreetly fashionable belt.

'Are you ready?' he enquired, eschewing any conventional greeting.

'What do you want?' Maria demanded rudely, not yet fully recovered from the oddly physical shock of seeing him so unexpectedly.

Luke didn't answer her immediately, but the grey eyes were eloquent as they dropped to the tiny champagne-coloured skirt the slenderness of her legs made permissible, then travelled upwards again in slow appraisal of her strapless matching bustier, encrusted with transparent beads and revealing both her smooth olive-toned midriff and the upper swell of her high, proud breasts beneath the single fine circle of gold she wore about her neck.

'Do you really want to go into that now?' he challenged her softly, his ironic gaze returning briefly to her party face and the shiny, streaky curls that tumbled over her brow and about her neck, just skimming her bare shoulders. Then he glanced at his watch. 'I don't think we have time.'

'I meant, why are you here?' Maria elaborated bitingly, suppressing reactions more heated than simple anger.

'To make sure you get to this dinner tonight.' It was tersely volunteered.

'Cavell never said anything about this,' she protested tightly.

'Cavell doesn't know.'

She had already guessed that, and her smile was blistering as she registered his arrogance all over again. He not only believed that she would be a willing accessory to his two-timing Cavell, but that Cavell either wouldn't realise what was happening or wouldn't mind if she did.

'Then forget it. I've already made arrangements to go with Nicky and Florian.'

'Cancel them. God, do you think Nicky really wants you hanging around?' Luke added disgustedly, his expression growing relentless.

'Does Cavell?'

'Cavell doesn't come into this. Get used to the idea, Maria. I'm going to be partnering you at most of the functions you'll be required to attend in your professional capacity over the next few weeks.'

'That wasn't in my contract, and there was no mention of it in the programme Giles and Cavell have outlined for me either.' Maria produced a whisper of a laugh. 'In fact, I could swear your image-maker wants me to come across as a free spirit, someone who doesn't need the convention of a male escort—and I don't. It won't be a pretence.'

'Nevertheless, you'll have one,' Luke told her inexorably.

'You?' Maria derided.

'Who else? Unless you've moved unbelievably fast, Nicky Kai still has a claim on Jones, and while some of the other jocks may have shown signs of making themselves available as reserve players last night—yes, I noticed the attention you attracted—they'll just have to wait their turn.' The look Luke gave her was cautionary as she stirred rebelliously, brilliant lips parting. 'And perhaps I should remind you that the contract you've just cited binds you as securely as it does us, unless you're willing to face interminable legal hassles in an effort to extricate yourself.'

'Why are you doing this?' The passionate question was involuntary and, regaining a measure of both control and fighting spirit, she went on quickly in a lightly mocking tone, 'And what's Cavell Fielding's reaction going to be when she does know about these. . .plans you have for escorting me? And not so much about the fact of them, as the reasons behind the fact?'

'You seemed to understand it clearly enough last night, so why not now? I won't have Cavell dragged into our personal affairs.'

It was offered as a warning, but the threat was unmistakable.

'Our personal affairs!' Maria sent him a smouldering glance as her mind screamed its resistance to the idea of there ever being anything personal between them, and every muscle in her body clenched in physical imitation of that wild denial.

Luke shrugged indifferently, his face hard but still astonishingly handsome.

'How else should I phrase it? I can be a lot more crude if you want me to.'

'I'm sure you can!' Maria snapped, and flung out a hand, unconscious of the helpless appeal allied to imperative demand in the gesture as control slipped once more. 'Tell me why you're doing this, damn you!'

'Why?' he repeated, his eyes resting on the suddenly tempestuous shape of her mouth. 'Because arriving with you makes it easier for me to leave with you—to take you home, Maria.'

And all that the phrase implied. He didn't need to be more explicit. She flung up her head, bright satin-smooth curls shaking.

'I'd rather die!'

It rang with pride and passion, the intensity of the emotion heightening the slightly exotic aspect of her peculiar beauty which was in reality merely the end sum of a wonderfully mixed ancestry of ordinary Celts, Latins and Anglo-Saxons.

Luke laughed, his amusement genuine for a moment.

'How extremely dramatic!'

'But true,' she insisted, her eyes still stormy.

'And passionate.' Grey eyes were turned silvery by a

gleam of speculation. 'Do you make love as passionately as you hate?'

'Love?' Maria scorned, and saw his lips twist in
acknowledgement.

'You're right—a badly chosen phrase,' he conceded
derisively as he looked at his watch again. 'The limi-
tations of our language. . . Ring Jones and tell him I'm
taking you to this dinner.'

'Because arriving with me will make it easier for you
to leave with me?' Maria threw his explanation back at
him. 'Easier being the *limited* English way of saying—
less likely to excite comment and speculation?'

'If you like,' he allowed tautly.

'And it will look more as if you're carrying out a
professional duty.' Surging resentment drove her on.
'So if you don't want anyone thinking you might be
with me for personal reasons, why bother?'

'You know why,' Luke asserted, suddenly harsh.

But she didn't really. Oh, yes, she recognised the
sexual awareness that was an integral part of his
attitude towards her, and it made her uneasy, but he
couldn't really mean to do anything about it when he
despised her so intensely. His talk was just that, talk
aimed at intimidating her, but she would never give
him the satisfaction of allowing him to succeed. Six
years ago, her own bewildering awareness of him, the
way it had made her feel threatened, must have been
obvious to him when his simple presence, a glance in
her direction, the sound of his voice, had been enough
to unnerve her; but these days she answered back—
and for some reason he was hell-bent on punishing her
for what he believed her to be, humiliating her with
constant reminders of his contempt.

But he would never actually touch her, Maria
decided, directing a quick look at the resolute line of
chin and jaw and the arrogant curve of his nose.

Strength of character and a confident decisiveness were implicit in the hardness of that darkly handsome face, and while the curve of his lower lip was disturbingly sensual, there was a fastidiousness there too which ought to be reassuring. He wouldn't be able to bring himself to touch her, because if he did, the contempt he felt for her would be extended to himself, and she thought Luke Scott was too intelligent a man to submit to anything so destructive. Like most successful, powerful men, he would cherish his self-respect.

She had no need to feel so uneasy in his presence. All she had to do was steel herself to get through the forthcoming weeks until he returned to Hong Kong and she was left to immerse herself in this new job in peace, free of the distraction he constituted.

Half convinced, she shrugged philosophically and turned to leave the apartment's square entrance hall in which they were standing, aware of Luke following her into the luxuriously appointed lounge, a long elegant room which ended in sliding glass doors opening on to a balcony with a view she had spent part of the afternoon enjoying, pretty green parkland dotted with ornamental ponds linked by a winding, deeply cut stream that was spanned by the occasional arched stone bridge.

A hand on the telephone receiver, she paused in the act of reading Florian and Nicky's number which was jotted down on the pad beside it, and threw Luke a challenging glance.

'Aren't you afraid I'll give you away to someone?' she taunted. 'Florian and Nicky, for instance? Suppose I tell them that you want to escort me tonight for personal reasons?'

Luke shrugged, unperturbed. 'Perhaps there isn't that much need for discretion. You're a beautiful woman, after all, intelligent and successful in your career—and unknown here. Other than myself, probably only Florian Jones knows what you really are, and he at any rate obviously doesn't find the reality at all unpalatable.'

Maria's eyes flashed. 'Oh, yes, Florian knows what I am, Mr Scott. You don't.'

'Get on with it,' he urged her impatiently, indicating the telephone, and she did, speaking swiftly when Florian answered.

'Flo? Did Nicky tell you what we arranged? Yes, only you don't need to call for me after all. Mr Scott is here, so I'll go with him and see you later. . . Satisfied?' she added sweetly as she replaced the receiver, finding Luke still watching her.

'Nicky's present naïveté surprises me slightly,' he observed. 'But perhaps she has yet to realise what she's letting herself in for, using her name to get you installed here, allowing you to share their transport. . . It's a very cosy set-up, as you admitted last night, but I don't suppose she knows what it's leading up to, if Jones has conveniently forgotten to mention the exact nature of your past relationship.'

'I don't know why you're surprised, when you seem to expect other people to be naïve enough to remain blind to what you're trying to do,' Maria flared edgily, thinking of Cavell especially. 'But in fact there's nothing naïve about what Nicky is doing, as she knows the nature of our relationship perfectly well. She's simply being as welcoming and hospitable as I've always heard the Taiwanese are, and trying to help me feel at home and among friends because she knows what it's like to be a newcomer in a foreign city herself.'

'And because she believes your relationship with her lover is a thing of the past.' The suggestion was laced with condemnation. 'But it's not, is it? You can't leave each other alone. The two of you have followed each other halfway round the world over the years, and she'll shut you out once she realises that your affair is something you renew periodically.'

'In between all our other affairs, I suppose? Where do you get these ideas from?' Maria derided angrily. 'Apart from anything else, these are the nervous nineties, in case you haven't realised, not the sixties or seventies when no one thought twice about having lots of different partners.'

'Oh, I know people such as you and Jones like yourselves too well not to make sure you're safe.' It was so cynically dismissive that she was momentarily speechless, and he added, 'Shall we go?'

'Yes, let's,' she consented cuttingly. 'If we don't hurry we're likely to meet Florian and Nicky in the lift, and right this minute I don't think I could bring myself to keep quiet about the things you've just been saying.'

She was still seething when they got into his luxury car, hired, he told her, as he didn't keep one of his own here, his visits to Taipei being infrequent and usually brief.

'Has Estwick spoken to you about the vehicle clause in your contract?' he added, easing into the heavy evening traffic.

'Yes, but I've said I'll experiment for a while before making a decision. Taxis seem to be plentiful, and the fares are very moderate.'

'Too plentiful. Along with all the motorbikes, they contribute to the traffic problem which is probably one of the worst in the world, and certainly one of Taiwan's major problems, along with an over-competitive educational system and political isolation.'

'I've never seen so many motorbikes at once before,' Maria confessed, staring disbelievingly at one in the lane alongside, two small children wedged between youthful-looking adults. 'I checked out the problems before accepting this job, but the virtues seemed to balance them, which is usually the way anywhere.'

'Cleanliness, low unemployment and crime rates,' Luke suggested.

'They were among the things that attracted me.'

'But Jones was the real attraction, presumably.'

Maria drew a sharp breath. 'Why does there have to be a man in it somewhere?' she demanded.

'There's always a man with women like you.' It was deliberately offensive.

'Is that what this is all about?' she demanded. 'Except that you admitted last night that you don't lead an absolutely pure life yourself, I could almost believe that you're one of those buttoned-up celibates, offended by the mere idea of any sort of relationship, even if it's between other people.'

Luke laughed. 'No, Maria, I'm not celibate, but I'm probably more discriminating than you are, and I've always avoided triangles.'

'Your hypocrisy is incredible!' Temper sharpened her voice. 'If that's the creed you apply to your relationships, why are you doing this?'

'Why not? You and I are both free, there's no husband or wife languishing somewhere in the background, no children involved.'

'Oh, of course, a piece of paper, a ring and a blessing make all the difference!' She slanted him a scornful glance. 'So why doesn't Nicky Kai come in for a share of all this moral condemnation, since you know that Florian is still legally married?'

'The marriage may exist legally, but hardly in fact. He hasn't been back to South Africa in years.' He paused. 'But it was very much a fact when you were first involved with him, wasn't it? His young wife was pregnant. Presumably you were the cause of their separation. Why was there no divorce?'

'Rachel and her family don't believe in it,' Maria snapped. 'And it suits Florian because it gives him a valid excuse when the women he gets involved with start talking about marriage.'

'You know him very well, don't you?' He slid her a contemplative look. 'Does it suit you equally well?'

'It doesn't matter to me one way or the other. You're wrong about me, Mr Scott,' she went on flatly. 'I could tell you how and why, but I'm not going to, because I don't care what you believe. Your thoughts and opinions just don't matter to me.'

She hadn't thought it out properly before, but it hit her squarely and solidly now. She would not explain herself to Luke Scott, because to do so would mean he mattered to her, and to let him matter in even the smallest way was to make herself vulnerable—to let him in at some level, and she had an intuitive sense of the havoc he could wreak once admitted to the number of those people who mattered in her life in their various ways.

Not that there was any real danger of his ever mattering to her. How could he? She hated him.

The dark grey eyes that glanced her way just before they moved across the chaotic intersection seemed to mirror that hatred, and she recoiled slightly.

'Is it that you can't think of anything plausible, or simply that you refuse to make excuses for what you are?' he wondered insultingly. 'I could almost admire you for it if it's the latter.'

'Almost, but not quite,' she jeered in a brittle voice. 'Because I'm still what you believe I am, still chasing Florian Jones around the world! Only, again, why does that make me worse than Nicky? As you've conceded, Florian's marriage is no longer a fact except on paper, and Nicky isn't his wife.'

'It doesn't make you worse, it just makes you weak,'

he told her insolently. 'I've never been able to respect people who go back. Going back, starting over, is always either the easy option or a negative step in itself, retrogressive. It's weakness. . . But then Florian Jones is your one great weakness, I suppose, since it's obvious that you haven't learnt a thing in the years since you first got involved with him. Or is it that your other relationships keep proving unsatisfactory, driving you back to him?'

'My hundreds of other relationships, don't you mean, Mr Scott?' Maria prompted caustically.

In fact, only one serious relationship lay behind her, with a Wellington actor who read news bulletins in order to eat, and it had died owing to lack of feeling, disappointing them both at the time, but Maria had philosophically absorbed the lesson at the heart of the sad experience. She believed in love, but she had been too impatient, her eagerness to experience it persuading her to believe that what she had felt went deeper than liking and a mild physical attraction. In future, she would not go looking for love, or trying to manufacture it out of other lesser emotions, but she still believed it would find her one day.

'Hundreds?' Luke was drily sceptical. 'How have you found time to make such a success of your career? How many really?'

'One,' Maria admitted shortly, despising herself for confiding even that much. 'It didn't work out.'

'Why not? No, don't tell me. He didn't measure up to Jones, the affair lacked the romance of having to follow a man around the world—perhaps even the bitter-sweet romance of uncertainty.'

'There's nothing romantic about my relationship with Florian,' Maria asserted abruptly.

'Wasn't it a romantic gesture, accepting this job?' Luke was slowing the car as they arrived at the

restaurant, one of the most famous in Taipei, Maria
knew, and an immaculately uniformed parking attendant was approaching. 'And wasn't he being romantic
when he suggested that we consider you for this job?
Which of you is responsible for the long periods of
separation, or are they merely dictated by your
careers?'

'I'm sure you've made up your mind as to the answer
to that, along with everything else, Mr Scott,' she
responded levelly, disconcerted by a need to conceal
an unexpected surge of bitter frustration.

'No, I've only made a guess,' he returned coolly.

'As your guesses instantly become convictions. . .'
she shrugged, not bothering to complete it, and neither
of them spoke again until a commissionaire had ush-
ered them into the foyer of the building housing the
restaurant and they were inside a lift.

'Just one more thing before we become part of a
crowd, Maria,' said Luke as the door slid shut and they
began to move smoothly upwards.

'What?'

The abrupt challenge was distracted because she was
struggling to contend with an unexpectedly physical
reaction to finding herself alone with him in such a
confined space. It had happened before, when they had
descended from her apartment, but then the presence
of another person had diluted the effect to an extent
where she was able to ignore it.

Now she wished fervently for an old-fashioned
attendant to match the commissionaire downstairs and
the man who had driven Luke's car away to park it.

She felt panicky, as if something precious deep
within her was menaced by his closeness, and once
again as shockingly unsure of herself as she had always
been in his presence six years ago.

'I want you to stop calling me Mr Scott,' he advised her blandly. 'My name is Luke.'

Maria dragged a breath into her lungs and managed a tight smile.

'Oh, but people might think there's something personal between us if I do that,' she mocked faintly.

The arresting copper-toned features tautened. 'I've said I over-emphasised the need for discretion. Try it, and don't tell me you'd rather die.'

'I think I might,' she retorted.

'Say it!' He was insistent, and she stiffened resentfully.

'Why? Because you know how much I'll hate it?'

'Will you?'

Suddenly the tone was velvety. He was half turned towards her, and Maria saw him lift a hand and watched it move towards her, coming to rest against her bare midriff, warm fingers shaping themselves lightly to its gentle curve.

The odd fleeting stasis that gripped her was complete. Breathing and blood were stopped; her mind emptied, muscles went paralysed and even her heart skipped, missing a beat.

Then it was over, replaced by its opposite, restored life an explosion of rioting sensation. Her flesh was vibrantly alert, too sensitive, her heart thudding like a runner's, wild hot panic flooding her reactivated mind. A single beat of awareness deep, deep in her womanhood made every muscle clench in frantic denial.

'Don't touch me,' she said tautly through stiff, barely moving lips.

'Then call me by my name.'

His fingers stirred lazily against her skin, and she clamped her teeth together over a gasp.

'This is harassment!'

'It would be if you didn't owe me,' Luke conceded

indifferently, no trace of compunction there to soften
his mercilessly intent expression.

'*Luke*, damn it!'

Her mind made the sacrifice for the sake of screaming flesh and she conceded defeat with a blistering fury,
rage a fever in her eyes, darkening their colour to
sherry.

'Keep practising,' Luke quipped amusedly, and withdrew his hand as the lift glided to a halt.

Maria didn't need to look at his face or see the
confident way he carried himself as he stepped out of
the lift with her. His subtle satisfaction seemed to
permeate the space around them. She could literally
feel it, absorbed by her pores and entering her blood-
stream, an alien message of warning, invader already
and threatening ownership, but the acrid flavour on
which she was choking was that of her own resentment.

'Have you gone speechless on me again?' he murmured tauntingly as Cavell Fielding came forward from
the restaurant's extravagantly decorative entrance
opposite them, a slight widening of her sapphire eyes
the only surprise she evinced at seeing them together.
'The silent nymph you were six years ago fascinated
me, but the woman with so much to say for herself is
infinitely more stimulating.'

'I'll think of something.' Maria's voice was milky-
soft.

Only what? The intensity of her response to him a
minute ago filled her with self-loathing, but she was
afraid too, because suddenly it seemed as if hatred was
no longer enough to counter the threat he presented,
and yet it was the only answer she possessed.

Quite deliberately, she summoned the memory of
the anguish of six years ago, the job she loved summar-
ily barred to her and her Communications course
sacrificed; and she dwelt especially on the dilemma that

had torn at her then, the agonising conflict between her obstinate determination to pursue an uninterrupted career in radio at a time when there were no positions to be had in Johannesburg but possibilities in Durban, and a heart-wrenching reluctance to leave her parents alone when advanced emphysema was shortening her father's life so cruelly.

The hatred was enough, answer to the strange, stifling power that Luke Scott had over her, but now a new suspicion preyed on the edges of her consciousness of it, the shadowy suggestion of a conviction that the hatred had its genesis in something darker and more complex than the realities she was calling to mind.

Six years ago! Luke's words and their possible implication slammed belatedly into her brain as she was being introduced to the entertainment editor of a local newspaper, but natural incredulity dismissed them as more talk, just words carelessly plucked from an inadequate language. Maria didn't believe that the child she had been then could have fascinated him. If it were true, he would have done something about it. That was the sort of man he was.

Yes, there was something sexual between the two of them now, but any interest he had felt six years ago would have been connected solely with the phenomenon of the awe he had inspired, so overwhelmingly intense that it had reduced her to awkward, agonised silence every time he was around.

The restaurant that had been chosen to introduce both the radio station's new programme manager and image to the media was splendidly stylish, opening on to a lantern-illuminated balcony all the way down one side, décor and menu strictly Chinese.

Maria thought the evening went well and could only hope those to whom this launch meant so much were equally pleased with the way she acquitted herself. At

her side, introducing her to people, encouraging her to
elaborate on some of her ideas for the future, Luke
was urbane, expressing only suave approval, and no
one could have guessed at the personal contempt he
felt for her, not a hint of it—or anything else personal
either—allowed to show through his sophisticated
public manner.

She herself had not yet fully recovered from the
trauma of those moments in the lift, but it probably
didn't matter. Who was there here who knew her well
enough to discern and identify any flaws in her own
polished public persona? Certainly—she hoped—not
Luke himself, and while her acquaintance with Florian
Jones went back to their high-school days in South
Africa, she knew he was impervious to anything that
did not affect him directly.

'You do this very well,' Luke commented smoothly
later.

'I'd rather be doing it on my own,' Maria responded
waspishly, taking advantage of the fact that no one was
near enough to overhear them for the moment.

'Sorry,' he drawled with blatant insincerity.

'Why don't you go and talk to Cavell?' The suggestion was tartly offered.

'She's working,' Luke returned dismissively, and it
was true, she realised, following his glance and seeing
Cavell in conversation with a television reporter.

'So am I,' she reminded him pointedly.

'We all are.' There was something savage in his
smile.

The look Maria gave him was inimical. That was
what he hoped people would think, she knew, and so
far only she was aware that he was here, relentlessly at
her side, for personal reasons.

CHAPTER THREE

'WHOSE idea was it that you should live here?' Luke asked as he and Maria stepped out of another lift, this one mercifully crowded, on their return to her apartment.

'Oh, obviously it has to be something Florian and I arranged between us, doesn't it?' Maria retorted sarcastically. 'Naturally, being the sort of people we are, we felt no compunction about making use of Nicky, letting her sweet-talk the letting agent. . . Why haven't you warned her about me, by the way?'

Her mind was preoccupied with a moment just several seconds in the future. Luke had brought her home as he had intended. It had been impossible to thwart him under the glare of media attention back at the restaurant, and she was still trying to decide how to deal with the situation if he wanted to come in with her when they reached her apartment—and she knew he would want to. That was what this was all about.

'Oh, I'm not worrying about Nicky,' Luke dismissed the challenge amusedly. 'She's tough, she knows how to look after herself and her interests. In fact, the two of you have a lot in common. You've both followed international careers, acquiring a cosmopolitan patina, you've both been involved with the same man. . . Have you compared notes yet? And I suspect that you're as resilient in your own way as she is, so things could get interesting when she does realise that you're out to steal her man.'

'I am not out to steal her man!' Maria snapped automatically.

Her steps had slowed, as if in sympathy with her mind's reluctance to confront the looming moment.

Dear God, was this anticipation or apprehension, and why should she feel either? She had turned other men—men she didn't hate—away at her door before now without going through all this prior angst, meeting the moment with the tact or firmness it required when it came, but not before.

'You're planning to share him?' Luke probed derisively. 'The way you did with his wife? Were you equally friendly with her?'

'Rachel was one of my best friends from school.' It was almost a relief to be being attacked on this particular issue, because there were other far more personal ones to be dreaded. 'I actually introduced her to Florian.'

He threw her a sardonic glance. 'To your eternal regret?'

'Yes!' Maria said vehemently, her thoughts flying briefly to Rachel, for whom marriage was a trap in a way it could never be for Florian.

'Why, when her existence never stopped you?' he mocked.

'My *affair* with Florian, since that's what you choose to believe, has nothing to do with you—past or present—but why isn't it stopping you?' she demanded.

'Ah, one rule for yourself, another for everyone else?' Luke was still taunting, but naked hostility blazed in his eyes momentarily.

But they had come to the door of her apartment and the moment was here and now, impossible to delay.

She shot him an eloquent little smile and said decisively, 'Goodnight.'

Humour gleamed in the dark grey eyes as he understood her. 'Not yet, Maria.'

'Right now, Luke,' she retorted smartly, determined not to reveal her apprehension.

'Why?'

'Entertaining the proprietor wasn't part of the job description,' she offered, her tone creamy as she nerved herself to continue the debate if necessary.

'Even if it's the job I want to discuss with you?'

'It's not, though, is it?' Of that, at least, she was confident.

Luke laughed. 'No, as always, this is personal.'

'Then goodnight again,' she responded evenly as she inserted her key in the lock.

'Why?' he enquired idly once more.

Maria drew a breath and smiled resolutely. 'Because even if my personal feelings were a whole lot warmer than hatred, I hardly know you.'

'There's nothing cold about your particular brand of hatred,' he contradicted her. 'It's a passion.'

'Then it's the only sort of passion you'll ever get from me!'

It was too confrontational, she realised as soon as she had said it, seeing something spark in his eyes, the instinctive, age-old masculine response to the sort of rejection men would always interpret as a challenge.

Then he disconcerted her by laughing again, but the sound was laced with a derision she found intolerable.

'Does the occasion really merit the heavy dramatics? What do you imagine I'm planning to do? Seduce you tonight? As you say, we hardly know each other.' He paused, allowing her to assimilate it before adding, 'Having waited six years, I can probably wait a little longer. It's almost a habit.'

The outrageous claim squashed incipient embarrassment, and in her distraction Maria allowed him to push her gently aside and take command of her key, turning it swiftly. They were inside her apartment, Luke already closing the door again, before she found her voice.

'Six years? I don't believe you! You haven't been waiting six years, Luke.' The disbelieving protest was almost indignant. 'You couldn't have!'

'Incredible, isn't it?' All humour had vanished as he turned to face her, dropping her key on to the stand beside the door, his features stamped with hostility. 'And yet it's true. That's what you owe me, Maria. Six years—six years in which I've never quite succeeded in getting you out of my mind.'

'It's not true!'

Panicked, she didn't want it to be true, because if it was, it increased the threat he constituted a thousandfold.

'Why are you so incredulous? You must be used to the way men react to you. There can't be a man alive who sees you and doesn't want to take you to bed, who doesn't wonder what you're like, although some might be able to resist the temptation to try and find out once they realise what you are. I thought I could.' Luke's lips twisted. 'Is that why you're so sceptical, Maria? Because I didn't act, didn't come looking for you again? I'd have despised myself. I despised myself anyway, haunted by things as superficial as a way of moving, a combination of colour and shape, an asymmetrical smile, the chance attributes of someone who holds herself so cheap she'll squander herself on a man as truly valueless as Florian Jones, and ignore both his marriage and his other affairs. No, I wasn't going to come after someone like you.'

'Then what are you doing here now?' Maria flared, the insults having begun to register humiliatingly, boring hotly into her.

Luke wore an expression of distaste, like a mask, so hard was its set.

'Bending with the wind that brought you to me,' he quipped, the humour harsh and followed by a shrug. 'When Estwick passed on the fact that Jones had mentioned you as a possible candidate for this job and your previous experience confirmed that you were amply qualified to do it, I thought—what the hell! Chance, fate or whatever you want to call it was offering me the opportunity to finally get you out of my system. It would be worth it, if it put an end to such irritations as the inconvenient way I'd suddenly find myself visualising you when I was with other women. . . So here we are, and *that's* what I'm doing here.'

'Except that your. . .is it exorcism you're talking about? It requires my co-operation, doesn't it?'

It was scathing, but beneath her anger Maria still felt uneasy. She half believed him now, simply because she knew a man like Luke wouldn't invent something of this nature, but the belief was shot through with a conviction that he was talking about more than sating an inconvenient lust. He wanted to punish her for something she wasn't sure of.

'Oh, yes,' he agreed tautly. 'What do you think I am? Obviously your co-operation—your consent—is required.'

'I'm not giving it.' Pride raised her head and flashed in her eyes.

'No, it seems evident that it's not going to happen tonight unless your mood undergoes a drastic change.' He smiled faintly. 'I'm no longer even sure that once will be enough. I used to think it would be, but. . . God! When I think that up until last night I was even hoping that I might look at you and wonder what it had all been about—that I'd feel nothing! But you've retained that particular quirky beauty that calls to something in me, some random or rogue streak, and this time I'm answering. Your intermittent adventures with Jones haven't destroyed or even marred it. If anything, you're more intriguing as a woman than you were as a girl. You're smarter, with more to say for yourself. . . We may need weeks, or even months.'

'We? Didn't you hear me?' The demand was a little shaky. 'Do you seriously think I'd let you touch me, when all I feel for you is loathing? When you talk to me the way you do? When I hate you?'

'Quite passionately, as we've already agreed, which adds a certain zest to the other thing that's between us. And don't imagine that either is one-sided, Maria.' His voice had hardened briefly as he added the caution, but when he went on again it was low and musing. 'Hatred and desire. Passion plus passion. It could be an explosive mixture.'

'Desire?' she prompted scornfully. 'Not this side!'

'No, that's also mutual.' The glitter in his eyes set off a jangling alarm in her mind. 'That's what it was all about six years ago, why you were a bundle of nerves every time I came anywhere near you—because you couldn't cope with your feelings. They frightened you. Perhaps you hadn't even identified them properly. . . And they haven't changed. I suspected it last night, and you confirmed it for me when I touched you in the lift on the way up to the restaurant tonight. Like me, you've been waiting all these years, whether you knew it or not.'

He was closer to her now, and Maria took a step backwards.

'I didn't confirm a thing! Did I fling myself into your arms? Beg you to make love to me?' she taunted.

'You will,' Luke asserted, the prophecy blending a breathtaking arrogance with pure threat as he reached for her.

'You agreed that my consent was necessary,' she

reminded him, sudden appalling agitation making her breathless.

'Your consent to our becoming lovers, as the inaccurate word is. . .and I will have it,' he added in a low, intense mutter, almost as if he spoke to himself, as his hands closed over her hips. 'But I'm not asking for permission to touch you. I warned you, didn't I? This time I don't have to consider you. . . That damned undeserved consideration that turned out to be self-inflicted purgatory six years ago, and so bloody unnecessary in the end. For that, if nothing else, you owe me.'

'What consideration did you ever show me?' Bitterness drenched the question.

'I left you alone, didn't I? But I don't have to now. I can't, anyway.'

His grasp on her tightened, and as she looked up into his face, so ruthlessly intent, Maria felt the urge to go on fighting slipping away from her. Heated darkness was swamping her mind and anticipation locked her throat, while her heart knocked frantically.

Luke's hands, still at her hips, pulled her lower body to his abruptly, and it was as if their clothing didn't exist, the outer heat that flowed between them creating an inner one as liquid flame engulfed her loins.

It was too much, too soon, and she went white, the shock physical, making her shake and leaving her head oddly weightless. Her hands fluttered at his upper arms and then clung, her fingers digging desperately into the material of his jacket sleeves to prevent herself sagging and falling.

She had never experienced anything like it, instant, total domination of the senses, and she was lost and helpless as she watched the dark head bend, the taut face come closer.

'Don't,' she whispered, clinging to the last vestige of

whatever part of her identity remained to her, pride perhaps, or simple self-preservation.

'I must,' Luke retorted harshly, eyes darker than grey, almost black, his lips nearly touching hers.

Then they were touching them, and the fierce thrust of his tongue confirmed his spoken answer as his hands moved upward from her hips to the bare skin of her midriff, his fingers trailing fire across her flesh when they travelled round to her back and from there up to the smoothness of her shoulders.

There was nothing tender or exploratory about his kiss; there was only an incandescent passion and a simultaneous assertion of his mastery. He fed her this first taste of himself in absolute confidence that she would accept it, and an anguished sound came from deep in Maria's throat as she accommodated him, mindlessly obedient to the command of his mouth.

Locked together now, welded, this was purely a matter of power and its absence, history's eternal lesson of the powerful absorbing the powerless, as first her lack of resistance and then her wild response *empowered* Luke—to take, to give, to plunder or to reward at his pleasure.

Touching her, he owned her. It was a stray fragment of thought, swiftly vanished.

'Although only heaven or more probably hell knows why I must,' he murmured unevenly, apparently as an addendum to the words that had been dragged from him just before he kissed her. 'Why should I want someone like you, whose squalid dreams of passion can encompass no more than the petty attentions of a man like Jones? I appal myself. . .'

As the abrasive words poured into her ears, he was moving her against an ornamental lacquerwork cabinet of hip height and bending her backwards, a hand dealing with the intricacies of her bustier with a sure skill that bore witness to a wealth of experience with even the most esoteric of feminine garments.

Somewhere within herself she registered the contempt and forced a husky response: 'I hate you!'

'Yes, I know.'

It was supremely indifferent, but, even as it burned into her like acid, her fingers were plunging into the midnight darkness of his hair as she invited his kiss again, the tumult of his mouth on hers and in it already a necessity, wildness running in her veins, the heavy aching beat of desire unchecked at the deep core of her womanhood.

Luke's kiss, withheld to torment her for a moment while he stared into her darkened eyes, was an insult when it came, and yet insufficient to her hunger, because his mouth was torn away from hers again almost at once, plunging to suckle hard at one exposed breast for several agonising seconds, the message blatant—she was desired, and despised.

His tongue stabbed once at her nipple and then he was raising his head.

'I degrade myself with you, as you degrade yourself with Jones,' he grated.

'You won't get the chance!' Now she was fighting him, her conscious will restored by his scorn. 'Get out of here!'

Realising she meant it, Luke released her at once, his glance straying briefly to the proud lift of her breasts before he stepped back.

'All right.' But the reservation, or warning, was unmistakable. 'But I want you, Maria. I have a ghost to lay, remember.'

'You want to punish me,' she corrected him intensely, her voice little more than a whisper as the conviction lodged itself more securely in her consciousness.

'That too, probably.' The light tone was belied by the steely resolution that held his face. 'Except that I can't, can I? Because you want me too. We have something together that can crash barriers, go beyond the boundaries you must have accepted in your tawdry affair with Jones, since I suspect that he's capable of only the most limited kind of passion.'

'You don't know the first thing about my relationship with Florian!'

The words blazed from lips now denuded of artificial colour, their natural flush wrought by the man—the enemy—she confronted, but she made herself be silent when they were said. She would not explain. She would not let him matter.

'I know that in thinking he's worthy of you, you become worthy of him.' Utterly contemptuous.

'Which makes you equally unworthy,' Maria countered.

'Oh, yes.' Disgust betrayed him into passion. 'If I knew another way of effecting this exorcism, as you've aptly called it, do you think I'd touch you?'

'Get out!'

The unremitting contempt had become unendurable, although it occurred to her for the first time that Luke might actually resent her.

'There's that show at the Hoover Theatre tomorrow night,' he reminded her, excess emotion quickly controlled. 'I'll let you know what time I'll fetch you. Goodnight.'

When he had gone, Maria sank to her knees on one of the soft, silken Chinese rugs strewn about the marble-tiled entrance hall, to bury her face in her upraised hands but not to weep.

She knew now, consciously at last and with absolute clarity, why she had always reacted so intensely to Luke Scott. Subconsciously, she must have sensed the potent effect he could have on her, an instinctive recognition of the dangerous power he would assume if once she had known his touch.

Laid waste. The peculiar phrase, forgotten as soon as she had put away her school Latin textbooks, made an idiosyncratic return. That was what Luke had done to her. He had laid waste—everything; her senses most of all, but also her pride, her independent will, and even her anger and hatred, for the time that he was touching her.

She had to ensure that he never touched her again.

But how?

The heat of humiliation surged to the surface of her skin as she became conscious of where she was and what she was doing, kneeling there still bare-breasted, her attitude one of despair and defeat.

She got up angrily and went through to her bedroom and bathroom to prepare for bed. It was past midnight, so this was the start of Sunday, and Sundays in Taiwan were not going to bear much resemblance to Sundays in the countries she had known so far. She didn't officially begin her regular duties until Monday, which she planned to start with a meeting of all available personnel at the station, but between them she, Cavell and Penny Seu Chen had managed to fill up most of Sunday with their planning.

She switched on the bedroom radio, tuning to her new station's waveband—her competitive curiosity had prompted her to attempt an assessment of the English-language opposition earlier—and discovering a laid-back DJ playing jazz and fusion between taking a few calls from night-owl listeners, their character common around the world—shift-workers, troubled or lonely insomniacs, late-night revellers and cramming students.

But for once in her life, not even her beloved radio could distract her. Luke Scott was soon back in her

thoughts, and it was a long time before she slept. She
had switched the apartment air-conditioning off, dis-
trusting its effect on the health, and for a while she
tried to convince herself that it was the unaccustomed
humidity that made her so restless, but she didn't really
believe it, and the eyes that looked back at her from
her bathroom mirror in the morning were shadowy,
and hunted.

Or haunted. No, it was Luke who claimed to be
haunted. There was an hysterical edge to the thought.

Luke telephoned her early to tell her, tersely, what
time he would fetch her that night, and although she put
a frigid resentment into her voice Maria didn't demur,
since it was in their public, professional capacities that
the radio station's personnel had been issued with
complimentary tickets to the first Taiwanese appearance of a fairly famous American singer.

She had left herself the early part of the evening
free, and she had just finished dressing when Florian
and Nicky dropped in to show her some new photos of
the fair South African child who went by the name of
Joni Jones, Florian having insisted on the first and the
name with which he had replaced his original, paradoxically both more and less ordinary name, having been
legalised in both countries whose passports he held,
the United Kingdom and South Africa.

'You look gorgeous, Maria,' Nicky said generously,
also already dressed for the gig, although Florian had
still to change.

Maria looked at Nicky's transparent emerald outfit
and smiled piquantly. 'So do you, and I'm glad I won't
be the only one! I wasn't really sure about displaying
so much, but Cavell said it wouldn't cause offence.'

'Only a sensation.'

'That's what she's after.'

'Joni's a cute kid, isn't she?' Florian boasted, bored

when ignored, glancing indifferently at Maria's outfit before growing exuberant. 'Hey, I've got an idea! Have you got your camera here, Maria? Take a photo of me for her. You can be in it too, Nicky.'

'Isn't he magnanimous, Nicky?' Maria taunted, irritated by the peremptory command. 'Letting you share the limelight! Don't be such a baby, Florian.'

'Ah, come on, Maria,' urged Florian. 'Just get your camera—I know you always have one. It won't take a minute.'

'And you'll hold your breath until you turn blue if I won't, I suppose?'

Nicky Kai laughed in response to the apologetic look Maria threw her. 'No, he'll just nag until you give in out of sheer boredom, and probably also make us all late for this evening's affair.'

'I remember,' Maria returned feelingly, giving Florian a disgusted look as she left the room.

'On the couch, I think,' he said when she came back with her newest camera, photography being one of her most seriously pursued hobbies.

'I must let Rachel know my new address,' she reminded herself as Florian arranged himself.

'Then you can send the photo with your letter when you write,' he said as the doorbell rang.

Maria stiffened. 'That will be Luke Scott—he's my escort again.'

'Then Nicky and I won't hang around. Don't sound so worried,' Florian added. 'We're usually quite civilised when circumstances make an encounter unavoidable. Go and let him in, Nicky, while Maria takes some happy snaps quickly.'

Her hands were shaking as she obliged, so the photos were going to be blurred, and she put the camera down hastily when Nicky returned to the lounge with Luke.

He greeted Florian coolly, yet the glance he sent Maria was scorching as she murmured unintelligibly.

'We were just taking some reciprocal photos for my kid,' Florian explained insouciantly as he stood up, indicating the photos of Joni scattered over the glass-topped coffee-table. 'Maria's goddaughter, incidentally. You could help us out, in fact, if Maria doesn't mind handing her precious camera over. Daddy and the two women in his life. Come here, girls.'

Maria was nearest to him, and he pulled her into the circle of one arm, holding out the other to Nicky.

'Not the most brilliant thought you've ever had, Flo,' Maria ventured tartly, moving away again, avoiding Luke's eyes although she could literally feel the weight of his attention on her.

'Among the worst,' Nicky supported her calmly. 'It wouldn't be right.'

'I don't mind,' Luke said indifferently.

'Oh, they're both still worrying about the amount of flesh they're showing, as if Joni would mind!' Florian said cheerfully, directing a would-be 'men together in the face of feminine foibles' grin at Luke.

'Rachel and her parents might,' Maria retorted, and he grimaced in rueful acknowledgement.

'Anyway, we should be getting back upstairs, as you still have to change,' Nicky mentioned. 'As usual, we're probably going to be late.'

'As I'm always on time for my breakfast show, I consider I'm entitled to be late for everything else.' Now Florian adopted his spoilt-rotten superstar voice, and Maria couldn't help smiling sardonically, recognising the onset of one of his boisterous moods.

'Yes, I nearly choked laughing when I heard you were doing a breakfast show. In Sydney, I remember, you never got up before midday.'

A glance at Luke obviously caused Florian to think better of the quip she could see hovering on his lips.

'I'm a changed man,' he offered instead. 'We'll let ourselves out. See you later with the whole gang, right? Out in force again, taking the town by storm, Taipei's favourite radio station, dedicated to the payola. Just kidding—I mean the music. Don't forget to get those photos developed and posted, Maria, my love.'

When they had gone, Maria glanced at Luke, but to her relief he was looking down at the photos Florian had left behind, his expression inscrutable.

Her awareness of him was debilitating. She felt almost physically ill with it, nerves a knot in her stomach, and she couldn't dismiss the feeling because there was no rationalising it away. A real threat existed, because she responded to him physically, a threat to so much that she valued as part of her individual identity, autonomy, independence, pride, all of which would be lost if ever the weakness he created in her led to her succumbing to the dark attraction he held for her. It was shaming enough to be so acutely aware of a man who despised her, and whom she hated, but to actually yield——

She shuddered slightly. Self-loathing would destroy her in a way his contempt never could.

She jumped slightly as Luke raised his head abruptly and looked at her, his smile like a knife, brilliant and deadly, slicing at her.

'The arrangement is even more cosy than I imagined, with all these domestic details. And you're actually godmother to the child. Whose idea was that?'

'Rachel's,' Maria told him in a quietly biting tone, although she was still shaking inwardly. 'I might have known you'd put such a sordid construction on it all.'

'You'll concede that it is sordid? I just wonder what the little girl will make of it all when she's older. Daddy and the two women in his life,' he mimicked Florian's facetious phrase.

'Oh, for pity's sake!' Exasperation lifted her voice. 'Florian talks like that when he's in one of his exuberant moods. It's that flippancy that makes the listeners love him; three hours' broadcasting a day is usually enough to use up the excess, but he doesn't work weekends.'

'Excuses, suddenly? Explanations?' Luke derided in an unexpectedly savage tone. 'It didn't matter what I thought yesterday.'

'It doesn't now. That's why I'm not explaining anything more to you,' she asserted stonily, almost grateful for the reminder that his opinion must not be allowed to matter.

'Then if you're ready, shall we move, as I don't imagine you can bring yourself to offer me a drink before we go?'

'I'm ready,' she told him.

'Yes.'

Grey eyes swept the outfit which had caused her some qualms, but it was modest compared to Nicky Kai's, the oyster-coloured chiffon shirt collarless and slit to a point between her breasts, loose enough to leave them a mystery only occasionally glimpsed when she moved, dark nipples a shadowy suggestion. Beneath it, she wore loose silky pants in the same colour, pleated and gathered into a deep, fitted waistband and tapering at her ankles, one of which sported a fine gold anklet.

'Cavell Fielding approved it.' Maria hated the way she sounded so defensive.

'Oh, it's perfect for what's required,' Luke acknowledged ironically. 'Distracting, though.'

The way he went on looking at her made her flesh heat, and she took a second or two to ensure that her voice would emerge steadily before saying, 'I want to make one thing absolutely crystal-clear, Luke.'

'Yes?'

'I'm not a priest.'

Jet-black eyebrows rose. 'Anything but, I would have said.'

'I don't do exorcisms,' she elaborated shortly.

It amused Luke for a moment, but then a merciless glint appeared in his eyes.

'Why not? What's the difference? Passion as exorcism or passion as release and renewal of energy, which is probably all the so-called act of love means to your lover upstairs, if his partners are so interchangeable. . .or the little death as an end in itself?'

Incensed, Maria flung up her head, choking on rage, and but for her fear of any physical contact between them, she might have lashed out at him. Her hands stayed down at her sides.

'Love's little death,' she corrected him in a stifled voice.

'Yes, so that doesn't apply here,' he conceded tightly, his face hardening. Then he shrugged. 'You know I can't promise you what you want, Maria, especially now. Since you arrived, but particularly since last night, the haunting has become possession, the ghost a demon.'

'Oh, very dramatic and biblical! Is it supposed to intimidate me or merely impress?' Maria retorted scathingly. 'You really believe you're going to—to *win* this, don't you?'

'I do now.' His tone was significant. 'If I had any doubts before, you've made me believe it. Lust can be a powerful compulsion, can't it? I know, all too well, how it can outweigh everything else—the disgust I feel for you and the way I consequently despise myself, for instance.'

'But not hatred, Luke!' Maria's voice shook with the force of the rage and resentment his arrogance incited. 'You don't even know the full extent of what you did to me six years ago. It wasn't just the job, and having to give up my Communications course——'

'Being parted from Jones,' he supplied sardonically.

She stared at him, her eyes like burning lamps in her suddenly pale face.

'Were you with your father when he died?' she asked deliberately.

'Yes.' Luke's face was abruptly shuttered.

'I wasn't with mine! That's what you did to me! You deprived me of the chance to be there for him, and for my mother, when he was dying, because there weren't any jobs going in radio in Johannesburg at the time, so I had to go to Durban. *That's* what I hate you for, Luke. That's what I'll never forgive.'

Now rejection hardened his expression.

'I'm really not very interested in the emotional side of your family life, Maria,' he informed her brutally, and glanced at his watch. 'Shall we go?'

CHAPTER FOUR

'WHAT did you do today?' Luke asked Maria.

'A couple of interviews this morning, and I met Penny Seu Chen this afternoon and she showed me round our building, studios and offices, and we rearranged a few things in mine. I start work proper tomorrow.'

She had said that before, Maria realised, when they had left the theatre and Luke had asked her if she wanted to get a meal somewhere. No, she had wanted to go home where she would get something out of the fridge she had found ready stocked for her on her arrival in Taipei. Work tomorrow. . .

She didn't usually repeat herself, but apprehension was numbing her brain, making her stupid.

Because here they were once again, making the same journey between the lift and the door of her apartment, too short a walk in which to resolve dilemmas or reach decisions. She had thought she was tense last night, but now it struck her that she hadn't known what tension was then because she hadn't known what Luke could do to her.

Suspense was a subtle torment, stealing the grace and ease from her walk. She felt as if she was struggling through a nightmare syrup that suffocated and hampered, and yet still this walk was too short—too short!

She had spent the evening smouldering with resentment after his callous dismissal of her father's death, but now the biblical phrases Luke had employed earlier were suddenly hammering at her brain and heightening her agitation, although she suspected that she was playing into his hands by allowing them to do so. He liked her uncertain and apprehensive; it reinforced his power and it was part of the punishment.

They had reached her door, and instinct took over. Maria turned clear eyes, golden-brown tonight, on Luke and said what needed to be said, eschewing preamble, cleverness and a host of other possible costumes in which she might have dressed it up.

'No.'

His shadow fell on her and a traitorous flicker of anticipation stirred her senses. It was almost as if he was touching her already—but it was only the shadow of him.

Seconds passed before he replied. Then an ironic smile lit the dark coppery face.

'Yes, I'm beginning to accept that you intend to make a fight of it.' The condescension there implied that the acceptance was possible only because he knew he would win. 'Ah, but I should have acted six years ago, I should have taken you then when you were vulnerable in your confusion—as I supposed— involved with a recently married man, presumably for the first time, and not knowing what it was you felt for me because you were so sure Jones was all you wanted. As it turned out, you weren't so vulnerable, but the confusion then was real because it was all fairly new to you, so I could have had you then.'

Maria stood there, hating him, but not for anything he had done to her in the past. It was not a moment for remembering a job lost and parents left alone. What she hated was the scorn lacing his recognition of the power he had held over her, then and now, although it occurred to her that he really had been considerate—merciful—in leaving her alone six years ago. She could never have coped then. She wasn't sure that she could now.

'Go away,' she urged him in a flat, hard voice.

'Yes, I will, because, as you've felt it necessary to keep reminding me, tomorrow is your first day in a new job, and because I can wait, now that I'm sure of you. But in the meantime, you can let Jones know that he'll have some waiting of his own to do. I don't share, Maria, so he's just going to have to postpone the resumption of your affair until I'm done with you.'

'I don't have to listen to this!' Stung by the complete absence of regard for her the insolent words betrayed, Maria rammed her key into the lock with violently shaking fingers, anger stoking and stirring a seething cauldron of other emotions. 'Until you've done with me——'

'Unfortunately I can't tell you how long that will be,' Luke inserted drily as she pushed open the door. 'But I can promise you I won't extend it a moment longer than is necessary.'

'Necessary to you!' Maria faced him furiously again. 'My needs, my wishes, just don't come into it, do they?'

Fascinating in the way it hinted at both a deep sensuality and fastidious restraint, his mouth twisted.

'Your needs? You had all the consideration I could afford, and that far more than you deserved, six years ago. I was a masochist then. Not this time, though.' A sardonic gleam entered the grey eyes as he paused. 'But it's not really an issue, is it? Your needs are my needs, unless you think yours will outlast mine?'

'The only need I have where you're concerned is for you to leave me alone, Luke——' She froze momentarily as he lifted a hand, passing light fingers over the bright satiny curls at one side of her head. 'You lied to me. Don't touch me!'

'No, I didn't lie to you, Maria.'

But, as she took two steps backwards, he followed

her into the apartment's hallway, softly lit by the lamp she had left on.

'You said. . .'

Her voice trailed away as a fingertip brushed across the tempestuous curve of her lips, but when Luke bent his head he ignored her mouth, his own swooping to the shadowy centre of her chiffon-covered right breast, there to impress a hard, demanding kiss that sent a pang of piercingly erotic sensation shooting to the core of her womanhood.

More than anything else could have been, it was searingly expressive of the contempt in which he held her, because he had ignored her face where her personality and individuality were written, his attention given wholly to a part of her body—and a body was just a body as far as she was concerned, with nothing to do with one's emotional identity.

A body could also be a traitor, indulging urges alien to intellect and emotion. As the moist heat of the mouth working at her breast penetrated the soft material of her shirt, that pang repeated itself, over and over again, so that she had to bite back a whimper. Her nipple was hard and swollen in Luke's mouth, its hot stinging ache too much like pleasure, and she knew herself doubly degraded, by his kiss and by her own response to it, the pleading curve of her body as she pressed herself into his mouth a flagrant denial of the protest screaming in her mind.

He had begun it, but she was an active participant now, her breast voluptuously offered to the sensual onslaught of his parted lips when she knew she should be shrinking from them. Small, jerkily spasmodic movements stirred her whole body as she strained towards him, and he steadied her by sliding an arm about her waist, still intent on the proud thrust of the breast he was ravishing with such devastatingly effective skill.

Maria's breath came short and shallow now, perspiration sprang from her pores in an explosion of heat, and the driven sound of her reluctant pleasure and need could no longer be contained, escaping her in a low, shivering cry as she flung back her head.

That was when Luke chose to end it, raising his head and examining the agonised tension that held her face and the taut, smooth line of her exposed throat with dark, glittering eyes.

'I didn't lie to you,' he repeated tightly, withdrawing his arm from around her waist and stepping back. 'I'm leaving now, and I'm not touching you again tonight, because the next time I touch you I'll go on touching you. You do know that, don't you?'

With Luke looking at her like that, a combination of desire and disgust hardening his features and his mouth somehow more richly sensual than it had looked before, Maria had no difficulty believing him. The threat was real, and more potent than ever.

'Get out of here,' she instructed him huskily, capable only of voicing her greatest need at that moment, no more.

'I'll be seeing you,' he warned her casually, sketching a smile that went nowhere near his eyes, and then he had gone.

Maria locked the door and stood still, trying to control her breathing and slow her racing thoughts. Her glance fell, focusing on the front of her shirt, and heat burst to the surface of her skin as she saw the moist transparent circle left by Luke's mouth, the fine material plastered revealingly to the darkened, sharply erect peak of her breast.

Damn him!

The anger obsessed her, but later she turned it on

herself and found it mixed with shamed bewilderment. How could she? Pride alone should have made her indifferent to Luke's touch, at the very least; old hatred and new resentment ought to make it repulsive.

The woman she seemed to have become over the course of a single weekend—just forty-eight hours— bore no resemblance to the vague mental picture she had always, possibly complacently, had of herself. She was not frigid, but nor had she ever been a slave to purely carnal temptations; because she had always placed a higher value on mental and emotional stimulation than on physical.

And look at her now!

Over the next couple of days she discovered that she had to be careful not to think about Luke Scott. If she wasn't, he slipped into her mind, the memory of her response to him both torment and humiliation, and dislodging him once he entered her thoughts proved far more difficult than keeping him out in the first place.

When she saw him again, on the Wednesday, Maria was half expecting it in view of certain events the previous evening, and Luke obviously knew it.

'Yes,' he confirmed drily, ackowledging her lack of surprise when he walked into her office after Penny Seu Chen had announced his presence. 'Didn't you warn Jones that he'd have to wait a while?'

Having anticipated this, Maria was able to meet it with a degree of control.

'Aren't you letting this get away from you, Luke? You had your weekend's worth of fun at my expense. That should have been enough.'

She spoke the lie smoothly, but she thought he recognised it. She had known, without questioning how she knew, that Luke Scott was not done with her.

Appropriately, he ignored it.

'How did the two of you appease Nicky Kai?' he asked.

'Nicky was attending some sort of state banquet. I understand it's a common occurrence—Taiwan's greatest beauty brought out on show to impress visiting statesmen. Florian doesn't usually get invited and won't go when he does. He cherishes his anti-establishment image. Last night he had a choice between a quiet evening at home and the outdoor concert. He knows I've no more outgrown the excesses of stadium rock than he has. He invited me, and I accepted. With Nicky's full knowledge and consent. Satisfied?'

A flippant defiance was audible in the explanation but the mockery that dragged at her deliberately assumed smile, making a travesty of it, was aimed at herself. Luke Scott didn't merit any explanation. He had no right to one.

But she had known this encounter was coming ever since she and Florian had attracted the attention of the photographers covering the concert at one of Taipei's main sports stadiums the previous night.

'The somewhat juvenile excesses, surely?' Luke taunted softly, coming right up to the desk behind which she stood, having risen instinctively when Penny had told her he was here—a betrayal, she knew, but she could not have faced him sitting down. 'But perhaps it was a nostalgia trip for the two of you? Did it take you back to that concert in Zimbabwe and any others there might have been—in Sydney perhaps— being there with him?'

Maria drew a deep breath and expelled it slowly.

'Nostalgia didn't come into it,' she stated shortly.

'No, perhaps not, since it's usually a response to things lost, or ended, and you still have Jones,' Luke conceded cynically.

'As a friend and colleague.' Her fingers toyed with

the ends of the fine saffron scarf she wore in her hair,
a floppy bow peeping provocatively from her curls just
below one ear.

Luke didn't trouble to hide his disbelief. 'So if not
nostalgia, what did it mean to you?'

'Whatever it meant, you're the last person I'd share
my thoughts and feelings with,' Maria flared, suddenly
infuriated by the open scepticism she saw glinting in his
eyes.

'Then share the facts,' he invited her cynically. 'How
long have you known him?'

'Since my teens——'

Maria broke off. Oh, God, why was she explaining
like this, as if he had a right to know? He didn't. He
didn't matter. She had decided that, hadn't she?

'When you discovered that you had things in
common. What, precisely?'

'An interest in radio and the fact that both his family
and my own were recent immigrants to South Africa—
and that's all!'

She despised herself for sounding so defensive, but
perhaps if Luke understood he might leave her in
peace. The bleak little idea diluted self-disgust, but
then Maria saw that her explanation hadn't caused his
expression to soften.

'Is he really worth it, Maria?' His scorn remained
intact, and remorseless. 'I suppose you must think so,
or you wouldn't be here.'

The weakness had passed and her chin rose. Explanations were for those who mattered to her.

'I'm here because I wanted this job.' Even that was
an explanation of sorts, she realised belatedly. 'And
I'd like to get on with it now, if you don't mind.'

Luke regarded her in silence for several seconds
before making an oddly restless gesture.

'How is it going?' he asked eventually, hostility not quite masked by the neutrality of the question.

'I'm pleased with it,' Maria responded warily, reminding herself that she worked for the man.

'And you feel the people here are pleased with you?' Luke probed.

'I believe they are.' She was cautiously confident. 'Although it's not so much I who has to please them as my ideas, since a lack of support would hamper or even prevent their implementation—but those I've already mooted have met with even less resistance than I anticipated.'

'Why should you have anticipated any, if they're good ideas?'

Briefly, his interest was in her as a person with opinions and particular professional attitudes of her own, rather than as a female body he wanted to possess, and Maria responded with relief.

'Because any changes, however positive, require adjustment, and most people feel more comfortable with the familiar.'

Luke inclined his head slightly, studying the tilted smile that indented one corner of her mouth.

'And yours will be positive changes,' he complimented her thoughtfully. 'I particularly like the idea of your making yourself available for an hour once a week so that listeners can phone in with their criticisms, complaints and suggestions.'

'And a little praise too once in a while, I hope, but I've learnt not to expect it.' She laughed more naturally than she had in his presence before. 'I started a similar scheme in Wellington, but then I did it at the same hour on the same day every week. Here I want to vary the times so that I hear from a true cross-section of our listeners, and those who listen to the graveyard shift, for instance, probably never hear the breakfast show.

I'll pick a different slot each week and get the jock on duty to announce that I'm doing it.'

'Yes. It's your plan to play at least one local release every hour that's causing the real excitement,' Luke went on.

'As long as it's up to the standard of all the other music we play and in line with what listeners' tastes require us to provide, although opinions will inevitably vary regarding both criteria, especially as we're a non-specialist station with specialist programmes.'

He had been watching the expressions that played across her face as she spoke, determination, enthusiasm and simple enjoyment in the challenges presented by her job.

'You love radio, don't you?' he realised.

'Yes.'

'Why radio?'

'As opposed to the one with the pictures?'

He smiled. 'Radio is the old-fashioned medium.'

'But it will never be obsolete.' Maria was firm.

'I wouldn't be involved with so many stations if I thought it might,' Luke told her drily. 'How many people have referred to it as theatre or television of the mind? I'm a listener to all sorts of radio myself. I like the stimulation of being required to use my imagination.'

'It reaches more people than other media too,' she suggested, never averse to singing the praises of radio. 'Especially in countries where there are large rural populations still living under Third World conditions, the transistor is usually among the most prized of possessions.'

'And often a sole link with world events.' Luke glanced at his watch. 'You've never wanted to be behind a microphone, though, have you? You could.

You have a good voice, fascinating, when you're not furiously fighting the inevitable.'

'Nothing is inevitable. No, I prefer. . .making radio *work*.' Maria gestured expressively. 'Management, producing—and I've even got some experience assisting studio engineers.'

'Being in control?' He gave her a contemplative look. 'Lunch?'

Maria looked at her own watch and then at him, the pleasure fading from her face. He wasn't asking her because he wanted to discuss the station or prolong the more general conversation they had just shared. That disturbing sexual awareness marked his expression once more, and she felt an answering tug of reaction deep within her.

'I'm going out with one of the jocks,' she excused herself flatly. 'He's going to show me this museum he was telling me about. It's got jade, ivory and lacquer art that's over four thousand years old on display, he says.'

'Not Jones this time, presumably?' A derisive note was back in Luke's voice. 'Yes, Cavell tells me you're receiving various invitations.'

'Your spy?' she gibed, recalling that Cavell had been with her when another DJ had telephoned to ask her out to a street market that only operated at night.

'You're using them, Maria,' Luke condemned softly.

'Do you blame me?' she flared unthinkingly, unable to deny it.

There was something cruel about the smile flickering around his mouth.

'What are you afraid of?'

Maria hesitated, her pride in revolt. To give him the satisfaction of hearing her agree that she was afraid——

But she was afraid, of her own wild reaction to him,

acutely conscious that he would be utterly merciless in
taking advantage of it as long as he had no respect for
her.

'Not you, anyway, and fear doesn't necessarily come
into this at all,' she prevaricated stiffly.

A breath of laughter came from Luke. 'You're
looking absolutely terrified right this minute. God,
woman, what do you imagine I'm going to do? Chase
you round the desk?'

It was what he would do if he caught her that worried
her, Maria reflected drily.

'I'd scream for Penny if you did,' she asserted
sharply.

'I don't play those games—but I should tell you here
and now that I'll make you regret it if ever you try to
involve anyone else in this,' he warned her silkily, his
grey eyes suddenly steely and intent. 'But to answer
your question, why should I blame you or otherwise?
It's not me you're attempting to use, for whatever
reason. But the others could well do a lot of blaming
when they realise what you've been doing.'

'Hadn't you better warn them about me, then?' The
taunt was bitter.

'What for? They're experienced adults, not innocent
young boys,' Luke said dismissively. 'Presumably
they're attracted to you, one way or another, so any
warnings should come from you, and there's only one
that seems relevant in the circumstances. Have you
told them they'll have to wait their turn?'

'Oh, right! All these men waiting in line to—to have
me!' Maria's eyes blazed pure gold. 'I'm starting to
regret this desk here between us, Luke.'

The flashing smile it elicited was wholly feral.

'Come round and beat me up, then, Maria,' he
invited her, holding out a hand.

But caution had reasserted itself, a direct response

to his mockery. She knew how any contact between them, however aggressive, would end.

'If other men are attracted to me, then they're attracted to more of me than you are because they *see* more of me. They don't limit themselves to a single aspect as you do, Luke.' Her brilliant curls spun and swirled as she threw up her chin impetuously, the gesture one of unconscious pride, almost arrogance, as disdain hardened her face. 'But then perhaps you're limited anyway, and there's nothing you can do about it.'

Luke's features seemed to reshape themselves momentarily, his expression become one of savage anger, and he had taken the first step of the few that would bring him round the desk to her before she saw him drag control back to himself.

'But then they don't yet know what you are. But I don't think they really count for anything here except as some sort of shield you seem to think you require. But what about Florian Jones, Maria?' Hostility twisted his smile. 'What do you do for him?'

Shock assailed her as she made the discovery that his insults did not merely provoke anger; they had the power to distress. But then just looking at Luke actually hurt her, as did the mere sound of his voice, over and above the contemptuous content of what he said. The ache was in her chest, tight and hard, reminding her of icy winter days in Johannesburg long ago, when you laboured painfully to drag the rarefied air into your lungs at that high altitude.

'More than I'd ever be interested in doing for someone as one-dimensional as you are.' It was biting, but she was censoring herself instinctively now, because Florian's personality was truly one-dimensional, albeit in another way, and the only thing she had ever given him was the degree of tolerance his peculiar genius made his due. 'It really is a classic version of the old story, isn't it? You're only interested in one thing!'

A whiplash smile acknowledged the theatricality of her tone.

'What else is there? But perhaps it's more a question of what I can do for you?'

'Not a damned thing!'

'A liar as well,' Luke commented caustically. 'We both know what we can do for each other, so why all this frantic resistance, when it's obviously fraying your nerves? Are you just naturally contrary? This time I've got no crazy, pointless altruism restraining me, and you must long since have discarded whatever distorted idealism made you believe you had to be faithful to Jones in fact and thought, since you claim to have had at least one other relationship between your spells with him. We're free to indulge what's between us, to let it run its course, so why not accept the inevitable?'

For a moment Maria's shining head drooped, a bright flower bowing to elements beyond its strength. Was it inevitable?

Then she looked at Luke again, and hurt was an intrinsic part of her response to him now, a relentless ache that went on and on, without respite.

'Why?' she repeated his question passionately. 'Do you seriously need to ask, Luke? When you speak to me as you do, implying that I'm—— And why not say what you mean anyway? There are lots of plain old-fashioned words I can think of right now, going back to the Bible, some of them.'

'They don't necessarily apply to you except very loosely. It's waste I despise, that and self-deception. But what is it you resent so much, Maria? The fact that I'm not blind where you're concerned? I can't pretend to be, and you know it, so what do you want? Some

sort of courtship? Do you think you deserve it? Must I
fake an interest in your mind——?'

'I don't want anything from you, Luke!'

Alarm rose in response to the dark, angry glitter her
defiant claim brought to his eyes, and as he began to
move towards her, Maria also moved, whirling past
him as he came round the desk.

'Where do you think you're going?' A hand shot out
to stop her.

'To open the door for you so you can leave.' Blistering rage gripped her.

She had been just past Luke when he had caught at
her, and now his arms came round her from behind,
drawing her back against him, and the response she
dreaded was already weakening her as the warmth of
him transmitted itself to her.

'I'll leave when I'm ready. Fight this if you feel you
have to, Maria, but don't lie about it so crassly. You're
not even deceiving yourself, are you? You want me.'

'No——'

But she was too distracted to complete the denial,
and the breathlessness afflicting her made it unconvinc-
ing. Still behind her, Luke had bent his head and had
been murmuring his taunts close to one ear, while the
strong arms he had bound about her waist were tightening securely, making her captivity a torment. Her
awareness of the hard body at her back was unbearably
acute, and a shivering sigh shook her, but she didn't
know if it was governed by despair or surrender.

'No?'

Fascination held her still and silent as she watched
the slow, deliberate passage of the hand that moved
across and down, over her stomach, the snowy white-
ness of her skirt emphasising the rich coppery depth of
his tan. Then she was closing her eyes in an agony of

resistance, as if making that hand invisible could prevent what she knew was going to happen.

An aching pause, and he was cupping her intimately; a finger stirred, casually contemptuous, and a shudder convulsed her, a violent response, turning her rigid. Luke's fingers flexed once and were relaxed, and a bitter hunger was flooding her.

'Sex!'

She was tearing herself away from him and spinning round to face him, a storm in her eyes that was only part fury.

'What else?' Luke countered, his expression unexpectedly grim instead of triumphant.

'And you expect me to give in to it, to some biological urge?' Anger enabled her to see clearly now and drove her straight to the relevant point, eschewing futile denials. 'Do you think I have no pride?'

'Pride?' He dismissed it with a faint, scornful laugh as he moved towards the door. 'We all have it in some degree, but it's hardly necessary as a restraint here. Where desire, or anything else for that matter, is mutual, there can be no humiliation, no abuse of power. God, do you think I'd come near you, talk to you about it, touch you, if I didn't know for a certainty that you want me as badly as I do you?'

Knowledge replacing anger forced silence on Maria. Yes, she had recognised pride as an intrinsic component of his personal make-up, and the fact that it could permit him to ignore or override her resistance, her hostility, her hatred, was probably the true measure of his confidence in her ultimate surrender. He knew what he did to her. He had even known six years ago, before she herself had identified what ailed her in his presence then.

'You want to punish me,' she stated woodenly.

'You've mentioned punishment before, so perhaps

you think you deserve it.' He stirred restlessly. 'That's not what I want, Maria, and even if I did, what do you think I am? I want you and I believe you owe me, but wanting you hasn't unbalanced me to the extent you seem to believe. Squandering yourself on a man like Jones isn't an actual crime, and I don't have the right to punish it.'

'You do it with words, though, or you try to. The constant references to. . .to what you believe of me——' Maria halted fleetingly, abandoning the pointless once more, and then said the only thing he really needed to hear, simply and directly, without attempting to clothe it in sophistication. 'I won't sleep with a man who doesn't respect me.'

'And a man you hate, don't forget,' he reminded her mockingly.

'Yes!' Her eyes blazed. 'Did you really think I might have forgotten? I'll never forget, Luke!'

'Or forgive. I meant to ask you,' he added. 'Did you know your father was dying when you left Johannesburg?'

'Yes, damn you!'

Anguish coloured her voice as she recalled the dilemma that had confronted her, but no compunction softened Luke's countenance.

'Then I didn't do that to you, Maria, as you claimed the other night. You could have chosen to stay in Johannesburg.'

'But not in radio,' she asserted resentfully, her eyes dropping momentarily as the simple truth awoke old guilt.

'It would presumably have been only a temporary interruption to your career,' he pointed out mercilessly.

'God, do you think I don't know that——?'

Maria broke off angrily. She had dealt with the guilt years ago and put it behind her, but here he was, reviving it with his ruthless logic. She needed to remember that he himself had been responsible for her having had to face that terrible choice in the first place.

'As you say,' he taunted, and lifted a hand to the door-handle. 'Friday night. Cavell says you've been invited to the awards ceremony, and she's asked the organisers to seat us together. I'll fetch you.'

'What else does Cavell say?' Maria demanded tempestuously, hatred fully alive again now. 'Does she know what's going on—why you're doing this?'

'The personal aspect of this has nothing to do with Cavell. I'll be seeing you.'

Luke was ruthlessly dismissive, utterly without conscience, and she could welcome this further evidence of his hypocrisy because it reinforced resistance.

But as he stood there a few seconds more, holding her eyes relentlessly, Maria was assailed by a sense of what her fate would be like if ever she was weak enough to succumb to the dark, dangerous attraction he held for her.

Florian had referred blithely to Luke's owning them, with regard to his interest in the radio station, when in fact he was liberal in the extent of the leeway he allowed them, but in a personal relationship, she knew with sudden bone-deep conviction, his ownership would be total. He would demand and take—everything. Physical possession would be emotional pillage, her identity, free will and pride the spoils he claimed for himself.

She shivered, only inwardly, but Luke must have sensed her recognition of these realities, because satisfaction stamped his face as he opened the door and left her.

'He's gorgeous, isn't he?' Penny Seu Chen murmured with mischievous lasciviousness, drifting into Maria's office less than a minute later.

She was nineteen, the age Maria had been when she had first felt the power of Luke's attraction, and Maria regarded her with ironic envy, wishing she could have reacted as insouciantly, her awe and admiration as impersonal as Penny's, Luke confined to some remote pedestal along with other out-of-reach heroes, contact undreamed-of.

'I think he's dangerous,' she said drily.

CHAPTER FIVE

A NEW dilemma had begun to torment Maria.

To tell Luke the truth, somehow force him to accept that she had never been involved with Florian in the way he imagined, might just possibly put an end to his—his persecution of her.

She knew that, but pride made her reluctant to even try—yet she thought she might have to. On the one hand, it would mean she was letting Luke and his opinions matter to her, but shouldn't she herself, her own peace of mind, matter too?

She was no longer sure if she could afford to consider just one particular aspect of her pride when there were other far more vulnerable areas, capable of sustaining appalling damage.

To make Luke listen to her—could she do it? Should she?

She was still unsure on the Friday night when she sat beside Luke at a table shared with Giles and Ursula Estwick and a famous local actress married to a slightly less famous politician, in one of Taipei's luxury hotels, the massive second-floor chamber in which the televised awards ceremony was taking place officially and quaintly designated the Ballroom.

'No ball has ever been held here,' Luke told Maria laconically. 'It's used mostly for conventions, and occasionally for events such as this, as well as cabaret and supper-theatre runs.'

In public he was urbane, and no one could have guessed that their presence here together was dictated by anything other than professional considerations.

'Awards ceremonies seem to adhere to more or less the same format the world over,' Maria commented, betraying slight disappointment. 'Successive pairs of celebrities, one to open the envelope and read out the winner's name, the other to hand over the bauble, live audience and viewers and listeners at home making fun of the acceptance speeches—brevity is brilliance—and executive types rolled out to ramble on about each different category, with entertainment acts in between.'

'Except that you'll notice that much of the entertainment conforms to traditional Chinese tastes,' Luke smiled.

'Magicians and acrobats—they make a change,' Maria conceded, smiling too. 'And I loved the dragon dance; the aboriginal dancing too. . . Aboriginal?'

'Native to the island. The purely Chinese came over from the mainland with Chiang Kai-Shek.' He paused. 'But people as well as their ceremonies are essentially the same the world over, aren't they, Maria?'

The way he was looking at her as much as the words and tone struck a personal note, and she regarded him uncertainly, unsure of what he was saying, or asking.

'Just people,' she agreed tartly eventually. 'Human beings—*most of us*!'

'You obviously have some doubts about me?' Luke interpreted her tone accurately.

'No, on second thoughts I don't,' she offered mockingly. 'You're human, although I'm not sure if you know it. Human beings make mistakes, but it never occurs to you that you could be wrong, does it?'

'About you? But I don't think I am, because you're human too, with all the contradictions that implies— hating me at the same time as you want me, for instance.'

'That's not what I was talking about,' Maria protested resentfully, just remembering to keep her voice low. 'But since you've raised the subject, what about you? You despise me—so aren't you degrading yourself by having anything to do with me? But perhaps it's some quirk in your nature, and you actually get a kick out of despising the women you get involved with!'

Luke's face had darkened. 'Wrong, Maria. My previous relationships have all been with women I've been able to like and respect at the same time as I've desired them.'

'All? They can't have been very successful relationships, then,' she taunted.

'But they have been.' Luke was arrogantly emphatic. 'Enjoyed while they lasted and ended by mutual consent when the time came to move on, usually because both the woman concerned and I knew from the start that it wasn't going to be a lifelong affair.'

'Meaning marriage?'

His expression grew cynical. 'Most marriages I've observed haven't turned out to be lifelong affairs, and those that do all too frequently end up causing more misery than separation or divorce.'

Maria regarded him curiously, unexpectedly chilled by the cynicism.

'And yet you must still believe in marriage,' she realised, 'or you wouldn't be so disgusted by the way I'm supposed to have come between Florian and his wife.'

Luke's lips twisted. 'Oh, most marriages would start off with as good a chance of success as failure, I suppose, if it weren't for outside influences, but there are too many women like you around, taking what you want with no thought for anyone else involved, and then hanging on once you've got it—out of sheer habit or emotional laziness, it sometimes seems to me.'

'The way you believe I'm hanging on to Florian?' she prompted bitterly.

'Aren't you?'

'No!'

But she could see he didn't believe her, and she turned her head away in deliberate rejection, refusing to sink to pleading for his belief.

For Maria, and perhaps even for Luke, the evening finally came to mean something when, having done his duty as an announcer, Florian Jones was called up on stage once more as the winner of the radio category in which he had been nominated.

'Not bad for a baby station.' Maria's brilliant smile was for a particularly attentive television camera, but the dreams sparkling in her eyes were uncontrived, as pure delight and ambition triumphed over all else for a moment. 'And next year we'll be all grown up, with lots of nominations and winners. This will mean a flood of new commercials too.'

'You really identify completely with the station already, don't you?' Luke commented as Maria was exchanging victorious smiles and hand signals with staff seated at other tables, their number swelled by the presence of Cavell Fielding, and Maria had wondered earlier if she was still ignorant of the personal reasons behind Luke's behaviour.

Returning to the audience, an exuberant Florian had abandoned assumed modesty and was pausing to accept congratulations from all sides, but when Maria would have risen to add hers as his passage brought him close to their table, a light touch on her bare arm stayed her.

'No.' Luke withdrew his hand as she turned an agitated look his way. 'A little distancing of yourself won't come amiss. The management shouldn't try to be one of the boys.'

Instead of subsiding now that he was no longer touching her, the disturbance he had caused deepened as she looked at him and understood that the warning was a personal one, merely dressed up as professional advice. He thought her pleasure in Florian's win was for her once and future lover and, presumably, that in her euphoria she was going to let him jump this queue of men he had convinced himself she had waiting for her sexual favours.

'I want to talk to you,' she told him levelly, her decision finally made.

He leaned forward once again, subjecting her to the unnerving illusion of being pinned by his shadow, trapped and oppressed by it, as if it carried physical weight, composed of all that he felt for her, lust and contempt.

'I want to take you home,' he retorted in a low voice.

The awareness turning his eyes lambent kindled a flickering heat within her, slow, soft flames that ate fatally at her will-power.

'If you're not going to listen to me, I'm taking a taxi home,' she asserted resolutely.

'If it's personal, then this isn't the appropriate time or place,' Luke returned, glancing towards the low, broadly curving stage. 'Wait until this is over. It won't be long now.'

Ten minutes later they were free, standing in front of the row of lifts outside the so-called Ballroom. Maria was aware of Luke studying her, although she refused to look at him, afraid of meeting his eyes. He made her feel naked anyway, despite the fact that there was nothing transparent about tonight's outfit and even its low round neckline fully concealed her breasts while revealing their shapely swell. Lower at the back, the short dress's absolute simplicity contrasted effectively with the extravagant colour, a deep rich crimson, the silky fabric moulded to every curve that it covered and tapering up to thin straps that revealed the pale olive tone of her smooth, slender shoulders.

The lift they entered was crowded, forcing them to stand close together, the brush of Luke's jacket sleeve against her bare arm adding to the difficulty of trying to sort out what she was going to say to him before she agreed to get into the car with him.

Would he even listen to her, and believe her if he did? He had ignored everything she had said previously to indicate that there was nothing between her and Florian, so why should tonight be any different?

A simple explanation, words monosyllabic if necessary; that was the answer, and if he still despised her after he had heard her, she was taking a taxi home.

The realisation that the lift was carrying them upwards instead of down made her heart jump horribly, and it went on fluttering febrilely as she stole a look at Luke, standing so still and confident at her side, and knowing, damn him, that she couldn't bring herself to protest or ask questions in front of an audience.

A few people still remained with them when they reached the floor he wanted, and he pushed her gently out of the lift ahead of him.

'Where have you brought me?' she demanded accusingly, her high heels sinking into thick carpeting.

'My suite is just along here.' He indicated the corridor and cast her an assessing glance. 'Didn't you realise? I always stay here when I come to Taipei.'

'Forget it—I'm not talking to you in your suite!' she snapped, chagrined by the way she had let him lead her.

He shrugged. 'I suppose you can say whatever it is you want to say right here, only I'm not hanging around to hear it.'

'Wait!' she instructed him furiously as he turned and walked off, but although his steps slowed, he didn't stop, forcing her to follow if she wanted to be heard.

'Aren't you overreacting a little, anyway?' he enquired coolly, still moving ahead of her. 'What wild suspicions do you have of me, Maria? I'm not going to jump on you and seduce you the minute we're behind closed doors. You'll have a chance to tell me or ask me whatever it is that's bothering you, and I'll listen.'

Subdued by the mockery, she joined him at the door he was now unlocking, still not wholly trusting him, and the gleam in his eyes told her he knew it.

'You deliberately didn't warn me where we were going,' she charged resentfully.

'I didn't think our destination mattered as long as it was private,' Luke countered smoothly as he switched on the light, but Maria didn't believe him.

The spacious living area of his suite was as luxurious as everything else she had seen of this hotel—a pair of couches facing each other across a low table, two individual chairs at an angle close to the window, with a desk and a bar supplying practical touches.

'Sit down,' Luke invited her. 'Do you want a drink?'

Maria shook her head, still trying to reassemble the thoughts she had lost hold of when she had made her discovery in the lift. Obstinately, she remained standing, looking at him and trying to shut down the traitorously receptive part of her that was assimilating the way his formal evening attire enhanced his devastating masculinity.

'I told you I wanted to talk,' she reminded him in a carefully colourless voice.

'And you didn't deny that it was personal,' Luke remembered musingly. 'What's worrying you? If it's the usual question of protection that so many couples can't bring themselves to discuss because they find it unromantic or embarrassing—heaven knows why, when they're close enough to be going to bed together—you can relax. Safe sex is rule number one.'

Maria lost her temper.

'You're assuming a hell of a lot, aren't you? That we'll be having sex of any sort, for a start.' Her eyes blazed, molten gold. 'We won't, and that's only part of what I want to tell you. I won't even agree to having you partnering me at all these functions I have to attend as part of the job—and I'll take whatever trouble you try to make for me—if you carry on treating me as you have been doing. The way you speak to me, the contempt—I don't deserve it, Luke. I came to Taipei because I wanted this job, not to be with Florian Jones. I'm not involved with that man in any personal way, and it's an insult to me to imagine that I am. I'd have to be incredibly stupid, or as shallow as he is. Apart from himself, the only people he really cares about are his listeners; the radio relationship is the only sort of genuine love-affair he's ever known. We work well together, I respect him as a professional, I can laugh at his jokes and I can even accept that his genius probably entitles him to live by a set of standards most of us don't even recognise as standards—but that's it!'

'Take it or leave it?' Luke taunted lightly, observing the quick rise and fall of her breasts for a moment before meeting her eyes and continuing quietly, 'Yes, all right, I can accept that. You couldn't say these things about the man if it wasn't true, and why would you bother anyway?'

'Thank you,' Maria emphasised sarcastically.

It elicited a slight, sardonic smile.

'From the biting tone, I infer that you think it's no more than your due? And you're probably right.' His gesture was reluctant. 'Because, as it turns out, you've developed the intelligence I expected of you, and I suppose there's some excuse for what you were at nineteen. It's an age when we feel but don't think yet, but you didn't seem to have learnt a thing about either yourself or Jones in the whole of the six years since I saw you last.'

Maria hesitated fleetingly, realising that he must still believe there had been something between her and Florian six years ago. It wasn't important, though, she decided. Surely it was what he had seen as her present stupidity that had earned her his contempt, since the past *was* the past, and she was still reluctant to explain anything more than the absolute minimum necessary to put an end to his increasingly unbearable taunts.

It wasn't as if she wanted or needed his complete understanding. Luke himself didn't matter to her in any way. His openly expressed scorn was all that had mattered, because, quite inexplicably, it had begun to hurt and humiliate.

'I have no illusions about Florian,' she confirmed drily, and was driven to hesitate a second time. 'That was all, really. . . If you don't mind, I'd like to go home now.'

'Why bother, now that we're here?'

The voice lowered to soft sensuality and the warm attention his eyes were giving her warned her. Maria nearly swore out loud. Of course, that side of it still existed unchanged. The truth might have stopped him despising her, but it hadn't put an end to desire.

Nevertheless, she felt compelled to challenge his assumption.

'I didn't come here to bargain with you, Luke,' she offered caustically. 'My body in your bed in exchange for your acceptance of the truth and an end to your constant comments about my supposed affair with Florian? Forget it!'

Luke's face hardened perceptibly. 'Do you really believe I was thinking along those lines? Why should I? You've told me what you wanted to and I accept it, but what else was it supposed to change? We still want each other.'

'Lust!' Maria condemned.

He laughed. 'Why do so many people use that word as if it represents something ugly?'

Her lips parted to tell him that it did, but hesitation seemed to have become a periodic tendency, afflicting her like hiccoughs.

No, lust wasn't ugly; many of her friends' affairs and marriages were founded on mutual lust and a few had stayed that way, neither foundering nor developing into something richer and more complex; but for her it could never be enough, even in the context of a mere beginning, and, after the depressing end of the relationship in Wellington, she knew that even if it had been allied to liking or affection, it still wouldn't have been enough. She supposed she was an idealist.

She realised how close to her Luke suddenly was, and panic leapt.

'I can't!' she protested breathlessly—stupidly!

Surprisingly, it diverted him.

'Because I have to prove it to you, don't I? That I've accepted what you've told me. By——' He broke off, an almost resentful expression flitting across his face. 'And how long will it take to convince you, Maria?'

A rueful smile tilted her mouth as she followed Luke's reasoning. If she was an idealist, he was the arch-cynic. It simply hadn't occurred to him that her resistance to their becoming lovers might be rooted in the fact that they simply didn't love each other. Between the two of them, the act of love would be a contradiction in terms.

The smile seemed to arrest him, his gaze focusing intently on her mouth, and after a moment he raised a hand, his forefinger extended, lightly tracing the curve of her lips.

'I just don't want you to touch me,' Maria asserted rather desperately, disconcerted by the huskiness suddenly invading her voice.

'And when I've succeeded in convincing you, will I get to see this more often? The smile, the single imperfection. . . Without it you'd be just another beautiful, exotic woman, magazine-cover material, for looking at. It's the human quirk. Do you know it makes a hollow just here?' His fingertip barely touched the place it should have been, but the smile had faded, replaced by tension, and Luke's eyes darkened in response to the turbulence that had entered hers. 'And you think I owe you proof, when you still owe me so much!'

His hand had dropped to her shoulder and Maria stared at him, immobilised by the fascination he exerted and incapable of speaking for a moment, for all the hot rebellion boiling up in her mind.

'Luke. . .' Now her voice had become a whisper.

Luke's arms came round her as if she had summoned him by saying his name, and she couldn't continue.

Prisoner or prey? Maria didn't know. She only knew that there was a part of her that welcomed this, increasingly subject to a perilous urge to surrender herself to Luke, and not merely her physical self but all those special subjectives that made her Maria McFadden.

Here it was again, his power over her robbing her of identity. She had never known anything like it.

'I'm not sure if I can do it,' he was muttering, his features hardened by some complex emotion. 'The time it will take. . .'

She saw the recklessness take over as he abandoned speech impatiently. Then her subtly coloured eyelids swept shut, blindness an instinctive need, as if by shutting Luke out of her vision she could barricade herself against the swoop of his mouth.

The pressure of his lips on hers was confident, demanding access to her mouth, and she granted it helplessly, already caught in the dark magic once more. His tongue stroked briefly across the tender inner swell of her lower lip, inducing a tingling sensitivity, and then she was accepting its sinuous thrust against hers and along with it a wild pleasure, desire following only a heartbeat behind.

Their mouths took heat from each other, lips and tongues hotly voluptuous, fiercely caressing. The hands Maria had raised to Luke's shoulders strayed eagerly to the back of his neck and up into the thickness of his dark hair, her fingers pressing themselves to the perfect shaping of his skull as she sought and claimed a deeper kiss, drawing him far into the warm moist depths of her mouth.

Her trembling body was curving and lifting itself to the hardness of his in obedience to the quickening in her loins, a fierily hollow quivering, the force at the centre of a storm of sensation. The intimacy with which she and Luke explored each other's mouths was possession of a kind, so wholly were they given to that long kiss, and when it ended they had to have it all over again, instantly, mouths colliding with an urgency which carried them dangerously beyond mere sensuality.

Desire was a leaping sheet of flame now, consuming Maria, the erotic furnace their mouths had become only an imitation of an inward eruption of molten passion that seemed to flow outward from the secret heart of her need, enveloping her utterly. She had no identity now, because sensation had torn her adrift from such restraints as intellect, emotion and an awareness of reality.

When Luke moved her back towards one of the
couches, she complied mindlessly, letting him pull her
down with him and turning in towards him as he drew
her across him, supporting her with one arm while his
free hand curved round her, instinct or experience
guiding him to the concealed zip of her simple dress.

Now she caught a glimpse of his face again as he
drew the straps down from her shoulders and found
her unencumbered by a bra. Black lashes screened his
eyes from her, but his dark coppery face was taut and
intent, angles sharpened, flat surfaces hard.

Abruptly, the dark head was bent to hers again, the
compulsive brush of his lips against the side of her neck
so searing it felt as if they grazed her skin. Maria's
breathing sharpened, uneven little gasps that caught in
her throat, and anticipation almost made her groan
aloud as Luke's hand skimmed her ribcage, moving
upwards towards the lift of her breasts.

Almost violently, she raised her body, ducking her
head at the same time, her feverish lips seeking the
scorching lure of his again, the demand for his kiss
born out of an intuitive need to let him silence her, so
that he might not hear the words and other sounds
which would tell him just how complete his dominion
of her senses already was.

So he swallowed her small cries, but in the end it
was not the safeguard she had sought, because in doing
so he fed her the taste of himself once more and left a
hunger in her which she sensed would last a long, long
time, if not an eternity.

His hand toyed mercilessly with her breasts, as if he
had the right; perhaps she had given him the right; as
if he owned her and she existed solely for his capricious
use. Hand and fingers so delicately possessive, massag-
ing the swollen flesh, sensually squeezing, kneading,
fondling, then palm withdrawn, leaving only forefinger

and thumb to tug gently at one hardened, burning peak. Maria shuddered convulsively as she felt her nipple rolled between diabolically skilled finger and thumb, the mini-spasm of ecstasy gratifying and tormenting all at once, and ultimately cruelly deceptive because it brought no resolution or peace, only an even deeper hunger that seemed to plumb the deeps of the most secret levels of self.

Passion ruled her, admitting no distractions, thought and emotion denied, anything that was known outside her acute physical awareness merely sensed. She did not consciously know that, with Luke's swift co-operation, she had rid him of his tie, nor that she was left unaided to tear at his shirt buttons with frantic fingers; and it was only through her senses that she knew when she came to hard flesh and soft springy hair, her palm sliding damply over his chest, fingers catching luxuriously in the light tangle of hair covering it.

The feel of him, the male realities of firmly muscled flesh and taut nipples which her fingertips were discovering, heightened her awareness of his masculinity, her thrill of recognition almost atavistic in its primitive pleasure, and desire reached a pitch so exquisite it was nearly pain. She seemed to be refined or reduced, essential early woman unquestioning of man's right to dominate, to take, the sexual politics of her century in subjugation to the powerful natural instinct towards surrender, its cost a paltry payment against the ecstatic rewards promised by Luke's virility.

One of his hands closing over the slender curve of her hip made her lower body stir involuntarily, the increasing urgency of the gyrating movement explicit, both statement and summons, and Maria heard the harsh breath he drew as he absorbed it.

Abruptly, he was motionless as a statue, but still holding her.

'Must I stop, Maria? And still prove that I believe what you've told me tonight?' A hint of strain was audible in the low murmur. 'Tell me now, or I'm not going to be able to.'

For a moment she couldn't react, couldn't answer him. She lay across him now, cradled in his arms, feeling the slight, delicious abrasiveness of his body hair against one hot cheek as she was held there, his captive, looking up at him uncomprehendingly, her eyes feverishly glazed.

The scintillating white heat of the flame at the core of her being was a governing force, demanding obedience to the passion that had lit it. Her lips moved to plead, but no sound passed them, and she glimpsed the flare of satisfaction in Luke's smouldering eyes as they flickered to her mouth, which was like a crushed flower now, a red rose, brilliant and vulnerable.

It was that look, almost triumphant, that called up resentment, which in turn restored sanity. Faintly, in some remote crevice of her mind, Maria could recognise and acknowledge the generosity inherent in Luke's question, but there was no place for gratitude among her present emotions.

'Yes, please stop,' she requested him huskily.

Now angry frustration replaced satisfaction, and she experienced a little spurt of apprehension amid the bleak realisation that he hadn't been speaking out of generosity after all. He hadn't expected her to make this sort of use of the opportunity he had given her. The pause, the question, had been a mere formality, the token request for permission men used to cover themselves against a variety of possible future accusations.

The reluctance with which Luke released her was palpable, his expression drawn into lines of hostility, and as she sat up, and then stood, Maria found herself deriving a savagely biting joy from the fact that she had surprised him.

He had not anticipated that she would still retain sufficient will-power to deny him when he had asked his empty, ritual question.

To deny herself equally, she acknowledged bitterly, still painfully aware of her body's aching need for fulfilment as she pulled the straps of her dress up over her shoulders and then zipped it up swiftly.

Luke had stood up too now and was watching her with glittering eyes, either unaware of or unperturbed by the disarray of his own garments.

'I'm not sure if I can wait the length of time it will take—but since you seem to believe that *you* can. . .' he added in an ironic mutter, and shrugged, the gesture oddly dismissive and yet decisive at the same time.

'I can wait forever,' Maria snapped.

It had to be true. She couldn't live with herself otherwise.

Luke smiled very slightly, as if he knew the desperation that lay behind the words.

'Just don't spin it out too long,' he warned her.

'You've forgotten something.' Rage, part of it self-directed because she had temporarily forgotten it too, made her voice shake. 'I hate you.'

'My feelings haven't changed that much either,' he returned indifferently.

If that was true, it occurred to her that he hadn't really believed what she had told him tonight, but whether he did nor not, it didn't alter the central fact that they were never going to be lovers.

But in the state they were in at present, both physically aroused, she trusted neither Luke nor herself should she prolong their presence here alone together in the tempting privacy of this suite.

'I'm going home,' she said woodenly, and added, 'Alone, in a taxi.'

'Yes, this time I think I might be willing to go along with that,' Luke conceded drily, his gaze skimming the new lushness of her mouth. 'The way I'm feeling right now, I've an idea that taking you home might prove too much of a temptation—for both of us.'

There was that ring of utter confidence again—completely unfounded. Disturbed, Maria turned away from him as he began buttoning his shirt.

'You don't need to come down with me,' she advised him in a stifled tone as she moved towards the door.

A slight laugh came from behind her.

'The temptation is always there, but it's privacy that makes it irresistible. Outside this suite, in a lift—despite the aphrodisiac connotations that have entered our modern mythology—and among the crowds downstairs? You'll be quite safe, Maria.'

Safe. It brought no relief. Maria was gripped by a conviction that she would never be safe again, in the sense that Luke had used the word—and it was less he who threatened her than the strength of her own feelings.

CHAPTER SIX

MARIA had finished unpacking and was preparing to shower when the doorbell summoned her.

Her tilted smile put the usual dent, something just less than a dimple, at the corner of her mouth as she pulled on a robe bought only three days previously, sumptuous emerald silk with an elaborate multicoloured dragon embroidered all over the back.

She guessed it would be Nicky Kai, eager to hear her singing the praises of her beloved island once more, and she might be willing to stay and share the light supper she had been planning for herself as it was Sunday, the one evening of the week on which Florian might occasionally make a concession to the fact of his breakfast show slot and retire soon after dark.

The sight of Luke Scott, casually dressed in jeans and an open-necked shirt, drove the smile from her face, but it was his expression and posture, both overtly inimical, that sent a *frisson* of apprehension running along her nerves.

'You're back,' she realised superfluously, her defences not yet in place because his presence was so unexpected.

Appropriately, he ignored that.

'All alone?' The taunt was silkily hostile.

'As you see.' Recovering slightly, she managed to sound defiant.

'Of course, tomorrow is Monday and Jones goes back on air, so perhaps he feels he can't waste his energy on you tonight.' Luke emphasised the insult by letting his gaze roam insolently over her robe, just as if he saw through it to the single garment she still had on underneath. 'Or are you waiting for him now? Was that who the smile was for? You'd sent him upstairs to make some sort of excuse to Nicky Kai? Wasn't a weekend enough for the two of you, Maria?'

'You only pretended to believe me!' she accused him furiously.

She had not seen Luke since he had escorted her out of his hotel suite and seen her into a taxi on the night of the awards ceremony, more than a week previously. Late the following morning he had telephoned to inform her that he would be out of Taiwan for some days as a problem requiring his personal attention had arisen at the commercial recording studio he owned in Singapore. His absence hadn't prevented her thinking about him, but perhaps she had allowed herself to believe that it would continue indefinitely, hence her shock at seeing him now and the panicky sensation of a shadow falling over her once more, its darkness an almost tangible threat.

'Whether I believed you or not is irrelevant now.' Luke had moved into the rug-strewn entrance hall while she was still trying to summon a mood adequate to the demands of the situation, and now he was closing the door. 'As is whether you were actually telling me the truth, or lying. Quite probably it was the truth, as I can't think of any good reason for you to have lied. . . But it's no longer the truth, is it? For whatever reason, you decided to resume your relationship with Jones— or was it just a weekend fling for old times' sake? All Penny Seu Chen could tell me when I returned on Friday evening to find you gone was that you and he had flown to Hualien for the weekend.'

He would have had to apply to Penny for that information, Maria realised. The Estwicks were in Hong Kong, Giles having been required to visit the

head office of one of their major commercial sponsors
to finalise the details of a competition the radio station
was shortly due to run for them, and Cavell Fielding
had also departed for the Crown Colony a few days
previously, telling Maria that whether she returned
depended on Luke's instructions. They had had a
farewell drink together, two women who had worked
well together without ever abandoning their professional personae, Maria because she had been afraid
of inadvertently giving away something that might alert
Cavell's suspicions where Luke was concerned. She
knew she had nothing to feel guilty about despite her
attraction to Luke, having resisted him, but his
relationship with Cavell was none of her business
really, and whether Luke finally confessed that he had
intended to be unfaithful or Cavell discovered it for
herself, she didn't want to have to feel responsible for
any eventual break-up.

The insulting nature of Luke's contemptuous attack
had lifted Maria's chin.

'Naturally it wouldn't occur to you that there could
be anything innocent about our weekend in Hualien.'
She made the words caustically challenging. 'Such as
the fact that it was Nicky's idea in the first place,
because she wanted to show off Taroko Gorge to me
as it's so famous, and that originally all three of us
were supposed to go.'

'Except that, conveniently for the two of you, Nicky
remained right here in Taipei.' It was smoothly disbelieving. 'Not only do I have Penny's word for it, but I
happened to see Nicky on television last night, partici-
pating in a chat show that always goes out *live* from a
studio just two blocks away from our own building
here.'

'That chat show was precisely the reason Nicky sent
us off on our own. The invitation to appear on it came

at very short notice, and even though she's no longer modelling except at charity functions, she feels a need to keep in the public eye, so she didn't want to turn it down, but she insisted that Florian and I should keep to our plans.'

'Very conveniently, as I've said,' mocked Luke.

'I don't have to defend myself to you, or explain myself, especially when you've just said that the truth is irrelevant!' Maria flared.

Abruptly she turned away from him and walked into the apartment's lounge, not consciously knowing why she did so, but driven by a need to get away from this man and the harshness of his condemnation, which shouldn't matter to her, because *he* didn't matter, but which nevertheless called up a churning confusion of resentment and frustration, as well as a new, unnerving hurt.

As an attempted escape, it was a failure. Luke followed her, the scorn in his voice flowing over her from behind like acid.

'Couldn't you wait, Maria?' he derided. 'I told you I'd be back, but perhaps I stayed away too long. It was unavoidable, unfortunately. I suppose you got impatient, left alone. Would any man have done, or does Jones still hold a special place in your affections? I suppose he was your first lover, and we all know what's said about a woman and her first lover. The difference between you and most other women is that not many of them are granted the opportunity to actually indulge their nostalgia, save mentally. Not many would want to.'

'In view of your opinion of me, it won't surprise you to know that I've been out with a couple of the other men from the station over the past week,' Maria volunteered stormily, halting and then swinging round to face him again. 'But it probably *will* surprise you to hear that I managed to resist the temptation to indulge my talent for marriage-wrecking and confined myself to one already divorced man and one bachelor.'

Luke ignored the sarcasm.

'You went out with them, but that's all, isn't it? They don't really count. It's Jones who's in the way here between us.' Luke paused. 'So what did you think of Taroko Gorge?'

The abrupt change of subject disconcerted her, but then she felt a measure of relief. Perhaps he had decided she wasn't even worth despising, although the brooding expression in those dark grey eyes prevented her feeling complacent.

'Stupendous—spectacular,' she offered distractedly, forcing her mind back to the mind-fazing wonders of the gorge running between mountains of pure marble and through thirty-eight tunnels, and even spanned at one point by a bridge of marble.

'Isn't it?'

Surprisingly, Luke suddenly sounded equally distracted. Maria stared at him standing there, discovering that he looked slightly drawn, while there was a hotness to his eyes now, as if fever or perhaps simply fatigue afflicted him.

An unexpected clenching sensation in the region of her heart shocked her. It had always hurt, merely to see him, but this went deeper.

'Did. . .did you sort out the trouble in Singapore?' she asked agitatedly.

But Luke appeared to have recovered almost instantly, and the smile he sent her was lacerating in its mockery.

'What a wifely little question!' he taunted before rejection hardened his expression. 'Didn't I tell you not so long ago that there was only one area of my life

I could countenance sharing with you—and that purely out of necessity?'

It was unexpectedly wounding, and Maria's eyes darkened.

'Which will just have to remain a necessity,' she advised him tightly, conscious of a sudden increase in the perpetual tension between them.

He flung her a savage look and asked abruptly, 'Do you still hate me?'

'Yes!'

The fervent confirmation carried all the passionate intensity of the emotion he had always incited, but for a panicky moment Maria couldn't remember why she hated him, and, when she did, the alien way in which her newly traitorous mind was functioning forced her to wonder why she needed to hate him. It had all happened so long ago, and she had found a successful career for herself in radio anyway, despite Luke's having caused her to be dismissed from that first job back in South Africa and the subsequent need to abandon her Communications course, and as he himself had pointed out—oh, as she herself had always known deep down, hence her long-ago guilt—she had *chosen* to leave Johannesburg when her father was dying.

So did it go deeper than that? She had accepted that he had had grounds for dismissing her at the time, considering the state of that little radio station's finances. Of course, the manner of her dismisal was still grounds for disgust—but hatred? Wasn't that too extreme, too personal? Unless she felt it because her dismissal from that job had deprived her of the sight and sound of Luke Scott?

Oh, it was impossible! Maria's entire body was rigid with the force of the wild denial. There was still his present attitude, the endless insults and lack of regard.

She could hate him for those, and lose any incomprehensible hurt they occasioned in the heat of that hatred.

She had to!

'Did you and Jones stay in a hotel in Hualien?' Luke asked tightly.

Once again the abrupt change of subject unfocused her mind for several seconds, but then her eyes flashed as she guessed what lay behind the question.

'We had separate rooms, Luke,' she told him tartly. 'Booked by Nicky, when she still thought she'd be with us.'

'Separate rooms don't mean a thing,' he retorted with a glimmer of a sardonic smile. 'Have you become lovers again?'

'No, we have not! I don't have to do this, Luke!' Maria added tempestuously, her pride rebelling. 'I don't have to endure this sort of interrogation, or explain a single thing about——'

His slight movement towards her silenced her, and she looked at him apprehensively, noting the way decision marked his face now.

'I don't suppose it matters whether you're telling me the truth or not, but I think you probably are. Why should you lie?' He paused, and Maria saw decision become intention. 'It's just as well. Do you know what it's doing to me, standing here seeing you in that robe and wondering just how much you've got on under it? I can't wait for you any longer, especially when I consider how long it might take to extricate you from another relationship if I give you time and you use it to involve yourself with Jones or whoever else you might have in mind. . . They'll just have to wait for you. I'm first this time. I've waited six years already, remember. That's why we're not really rushing into this, however precipitate it might seem on the surface.'

He was making intolerable assumptions about her

character, and rage flooded Maria's mind in a scalding cascade. Her initial instinct was to hit out at him in violent retaliation, the insults unendurable and unanswerable in any other way, and yet at the same time, some still, small place of recognition at the centre of all that red-hot emotion was acknowledging the kernel of truth hidden within the offensive words.

This crucial point in their relationship had not come too soon, for either of them. Six years. . .

'Don't touch me!' she said sharply as Luke reached for her.

'How can I not?' he returned savagely, his hands on her shoulders stilling her and seemingly stopping her heart for an instant. 'Six years, and then burning up this last week I've spent in Singapore, regretting the entrenched prejudices that stopped me making love to you last time we were together. God! I had this idea I had to be civilised, and wait until I'd obtained spoken as well as physical consent from you—and then spent days regretting it! I warned you I wasn't going to be able to consider you and any doubts, hesitations or scruples you might have this time around, and I should have remembered that. I can't afford to.'

'Another thing you've forgotten,' Maria supplied waspishly, agitatedly conscious that she had to go on resisting him. 'And so soon after we were discussing it, too, but then you keep doing it. I hate you, Luke.'

'I hadn't forgotten, and I've come round to being sorry that you do, but as it's unlikely that the hatred is going to change, and since we both know that this is ultimately inevitable, it might as well happen now.'

Luke's fingers worked at her shoulders, their warmth penetrating the smooth fabric of her robe, beginning to burn into her, and she felt herself swaying.

'No——' she began desperately, but couldn't continue.

'Oh, yes, I accept that you hate me,' Luke went on tautly. 'But it doesn't make any difference, does it? I can still seduce you.'

The utter confidence of the claim incensed her, but then came the pain of knowing that it was all too true. Luke could seduce her. He was seducing her already, pulling her close, and there was nothing she could say or do to still the instant leaping hunger he incited.

She heard the shaken sigh that was torn from him as he brought her body up against the length of his, and the urge to go on fighting him faded as she grasped at fresh knowledge, accepting the fact that this was entirely mutual. She affected Luke in the same way as he did her.

Mentally, she gave an ironical bow to whatever maliciously sadistic fate had done this to them, throwing them together and adding this towering, ungovernable desire to the other emotions existing between them, the hatred and resentment on her side, contempt on Luke's.

As she felt the sensual warmth of his mouth touching hers and then taking it, Maria knew that the situation was already out of control. Her arms were finding their way about him, hands lifting, and the pleasure her mouth took from his could not be kept localised, a rapid tide of rich sensation spreading and sweeping through her whole being.

They had spoken of exorcism, with reference to Luke's desire for her, but now Maria acknowledged bitterly that it too would be mutual. Making love would be an exorcism for both of them.

As a justification for indulging the imperative demands of the flesh it was pathetic, and she knew it, but she didn't think she could go on fighting the passion they awoke in each other. She wanted Luke too badly, her skin on fire and an even more intolerable conflagra-

tion deep inside her, stoked by the possessive mastery
of his kiss, an inferno of need, consuming her.

'I want you!'

She admitted it tempestuously as Luke deprived her
of the erotic stimulation of his mouth, opening her eyes
just in time to see the blaze of triumph in his as he
heard her.

She hated it, and hated him, but she was no longer
resisting him, so she accepted it in aching silence,
desire overwhelming pride at last.

'You always have,' he asserted arrogantly.

'I didn't know that I did.'

The heat of humiliation rose with that final admis-
sion, but it was pale fire, swallowed up in the flames of
the passion engulfing her and making her body stir
provocatively against him.

Defeat—and yet not truly defeat, Maria realised as
she felt Luke's response. Hearing his feverish mutter
of gratification as his hands parted her robe and found
her flesh unconfined beneath it, save for a little pair of
loose silky pants, she accepted a power almost equal to
his over her.

Almost equal, but not quite, because Luke still
seemed to retain a vestige of control while she trembled
wildly as his hands slid adroitly up over her ribcage to
cup her breasts from beneath, lifting them to the
swooping descent of his dark head; and she heard him
mutter intensely again just before his mouth took
voluptuous possession of the heated hardness of one
exquisitely sensitive nipple.

She thought she would fall to the floor, or faint,
standing there at the mercy of his ravishing mouth, and
perhaps he sensed something of her helplessness,
because he raised his head again almost immediately.

'The bedroom?' he questioned her urgently.

Once there, Maria let her robe slide from her

shoulders before stepping quickly out of her pants
while Luke undressed swiftly, tantalising shadows playing over his flesh, revealed and then tormentingly
concealed as he moved in and out of the circle of soft
golden light that came from the lamp at one side of her
low, wide bed.

There was a savage splendour to his aroused body,
and Maria called his name faintly, from far away, it
seemed, as blood drummed in her ears and he took her
into his arms again, sinking to the bed with her.

There was a fractional gap in time in which she went
blind and deaf and limp, a second that was almost a
miniature swoon in essence, but so infinitesimal that
she wasn't even aware of the fleeting relief, the madness in her again instantly, the craving, unbearably
heightened by this first knowledge of his nakedness in
contact with hers.

'Ah, Maria, six years is a long time to wait,' Luke
murmured with a faint sardonic smile as he registered
her frantic response. 'And it was six years for both of
us, but you'll understand if I can't sympathise with
your waiting when it was all unknowing—ignorance
being bliss—whereas I've known precisely what it was
that troubled me through all those six years.'

'Please. . .'

She sensed his need to avenge that waiting, but she
couldn't form words to protest, pulled in to him, her
mouth and then her breasts captive to the erotic magic
of his lips and tongue, the writhing of her body an
explicit demand for more. Luke's fingers were madden-
ingly light on her buttocks, tracing a complex pattern
over the smooth skin, and she gasped, mindless with
pleasure now and moving through desire to something
beyond, urgent and undeniable.

Fingers entwined in the dark hair of the head still at
her breasts, Maria cried out softly, shifting her position

instinctively as she felt his hand circle her hip and then
slide urgently to the softness at the top of her thighs
and accept the invitation implicit in her movement. A
finger traced the secrets of her sex, coming to where
heated flesh pulsed rhythmically in readiness, already
anticipating the entrance of his manhood.

A wild, violent delight that had intolerable hunger
as its other side spasmed through her as the deep, slow
throb low down in her slender body became a pound-
ing, yearning ache that must be soothed, or she thought
she would die.

'Oh, God, Luke!' The desperate words, both protest
and plea, were torn from her. 'You don't know what
you're doing to me!'

'Don't I?' It came unevenly, an odd bitter anger
roughening his voice. 'And have you got any idea of
what it is you do to me, Maria? What you've done for
six long years, and more especially what you've been
doing to me ever since we met again?'

As he spoke, he was drawing back slightly, capturing
her hand and carrying it to tumescent flesh pulsing with
vigorous life.

'Luke!' Maria's voice was reduced to a strained,
aching whisper. 'I want you so much. . .'

'As much as I want you?' The demand was harsh,
almost accusing, and his dark face was taut, pulled into
lines of resentment. 'I've never wanted anyone this
much—to the extent that I can disregard everything I
know about you and believe about myself. . . And now
it's finally happening. At last, incredibly, I'm going to
find out what it is I've been missing. . .wanting! All of
you. God——'

As she moved her fingers passion detonated. Maria
had never dreamed that two people could generate so
much sheer sensation between them. This was a rage

of feeling, carrying them out of themselves, beyond the confines of their mortality.

She had never known anything like the need that rent her, and she knew it was the same need that was racking Luke's rigid body; and still it escalated as they succumbed to a welter of tumultuous embraces, caresses and kisses, their staccato breathing punctuated by the sharp sounds of desire, their skin damp with perspiration.

Their passion precluded tenderness, their love-making nearly fighting, and Maria could almost believe that that was really what it was, else how could Luke continue to deny her and himself like this?

And yet, self-denied, he was still dominant, rampant male, she the one reduced to mindless begging for the release she now knew could only ever be temporary because she was an addict already, enslaved by him as he fed her again the fatal taste, the bitter-sweet of his passion, and her own.

The slide of bodies bathed in perspiration ceased as Luke shuddered and stilled momentarily before moving to kneel over her, surveying her with glittering eyes, his shadow cast over her, and Maria fell back against the pillows with a hoarse sob, wordlessly pleading with him to end the torment, aching for him, needing to feel him inside her, hating him for prolonging her agony like this and resenting the control that enabled him to do it.

Shaking violently in the intolerable hold of a passion as bitter as it was irresistible and torrid, she looked up at the man who had done this to her, his body before and above her, glistening and dark, darker still where it was shadowed with hair. He looked alien and power-ful, the master of her pleasure, giving and denying, tormenting while he delighted—about to become her lover and desired as such, although still a stranger.

'Does it hurt you to wait, my darling Maria?' he challenged her harshly. 'To be denied?'

For the most fleeting of moments, she knew humiliation, but then anger surged, and an aching triumph with it because she knew he could not deny her.

'Yes, damn you!' she acknowledged, her eyes blazing pure gold.

She reached up for him, clawing at his shoulders, her fingers slipping on his wet skin as her body strained upwards towards his, arching rigidly, jerking and quivering convulsively.

'And me, Maria,' groaned Luke, abruptly between her thighs. 'All of me! All this long time. . .'

Then their waiting was over. Maria was moist, hot and tight about him as he moved powerfully within her, and the exquisite friction of their joining commanded them utterly, carrying them upwards through rapture and beyond to a soaringly ecstatic climax so intense, so comprehensive that Maria felt it expanding to embrace her mind, spirit and emotions.

Nothing was omitted, no aspect of her being was not party to this miraculous moment of ultimate sharing, and in the final vibration of the after-shock set up by the last incredible convulsion of ecstasy, she heard Luke gasping her name and understood that she didn't hate him and never had.

Resentment. That was what it had been, what she had felt all along, she accepted a little later when she was in a state to sort and make sense of shocking new knowledge. She had always resented Luke, and feared the way he made her feel—because she must have sensed from the beginning the power he could and did have over her; because he had deprived her of himself when he had had her dismissed from that very first job back in South Africa; because something had led him to misjudge and despise her, and he was unable to see the truth; because she had always known that he could break her heart. . .

As he had just broken it. Her looted heart, first ransacked of all that she had to give and then shattered.

Having spent himself, he had still found the will and strength to move away after he had withdrawn from her, so that they lay without touching, the space between them painfully eloquent, the gleaming coppery curve of the shoulder that he presented to her even more hurtful.

'Bastard,' Maria said softly, noticing the marks her nails had left in his smooth flesh without surprise.

'Didn't you enjoy it?' Luke enquired in a sarcastic murmur, not even turning to look at her.

She sat up, measuring the distance from the bed to her discarded robe lying on the soft carpet. Sighing, she ignored pride's dictates and sank back against the pillows.

'You know I did,' she conceded bleakly, and added flatly, 'And I hate myself.'

'Don't worry, you'll soon get over it and revert to hating me,' he offered lazily, still turned away from her. 'It's always easier to hate others than it is to hate ourselves.'

'Is that why you despise me?' she retorted, languidly caustic. 'So that you don't have to despise yourself?'

Luke was silent for several seconds and she began to suspect that he had fallen asleep.

Then he said tiredly, 'What makes you think I don't? Stop talking so much, Maria. It was only sex, after all.'

For him. And she had also thought that was all it was, she acknowledged wearily. Fool!

'If I had any energy left, I'd throw you out,' she told him resentfully.

'If I had any, I'd walk out,' he countered.

'You were right, I hate you again!'

'Don't talk unless you've got something new to tell me.'

Maria subsided. It was a strange conversation, slee-pily hostile, with both of them drained by the extrava-gant expenditure of passion that had gone before. She had told him the truth, she discovered, staring at the polished beauty of his shoulder. It was possible to hate at the same time as you loved.

She drifted into sleep, resisting an urge to move closer and press her mouth to his shoulder, combating it by wondering what his reaction might be if she should succumb to an opposing temptation and sink her teeth into the flesh her nails had already marred.

When she woke again, in the early hours of Monday morning, Luke and gone, but she thought he would be back. How could anyone walk away from the sort of passion that existed between them?

But he didn't come, either to her apartment or to her office. He didn't come that day, or the next, and a host of mocking little phrases found their insidious way into her mind.

He had sated his lust, cast out the demon, exorcised the ghost.

Maria was forced to begin believing that they repre-sented the truth on the Thursday when, having first steeled herself to sound casual, she mentioned to Giles Estwick that Luke didn't seem to be around any longer.

'He was in Singapore last week, but he came back at the weekend, I know,' she observed innocently, hating herself for needing to know so badly. 'Has he left again?'

'He's back in Hong Kong.' Giles had returned from the Colony the previous day. 'In fact, Ursula and I accepted his invitation to go over to Macau with him and Cavell Fielding on Tuesday evening for dinner and a spot of gambling in one of the casinos, and a very enjoyable few hours they were too.'

Maria kept her face expressionless, but she felt as if merciless fingers were mangling her heart.

Clearly Luke had achieved the exorcism he had sought by making love to her and was now free to either pursue or resume a relationship with Cavell Fielding, with no danger of damage to his self-respect because he respected Cavell.

Whereas she—Maria's lips tightened, confining a moan of self-disgust. He had used the word necessity in speaking of his desire for her. She had been necessary, but despised, so naturally he had discarded her the moment she was no longer necessary to him, and their single sexual collision was all it had taken to free him.

She hadn't been so lucky. Instead of soothing desire forever, the shattering culmination of their abandonment to passion had renewed and exacerbated it. Knowledge had betrayed her, because now she would always know what she was missing, and she would never be free again.

Unlike Luke, who had taken his freedom at her expense. Or had she given it to him?

A savage anger rose, but she must have kept it hidden, because Giles didn't appear to notice anything wrong.

When he had left, she was still prevented from giving way to rage as Penny put through one of the DJs she had already been out with once, ringing to ask if she would like to go to a Mongolian barbecue with him that evening.

'Sounds good to me,' Maria accepted decisively, a light of blazing defiance in her eyes.

Only she wasn't sure at whom the defiance was directed, Luke or herself. She had to suppose it was herself. Now that Luke no longer wanted her, he wouldn't care about anything she did, so no action of hers constituted defiance.

Self-recrimination was setting in. Maria burned with shame. How could she have done this to herself? How could she have let herself be used by a man who held her in contempt? Worse, she had been prepared to let him go on using her, had he chosen to do so.

That was why she was reacting so badly to the news that he had left Taipei.

Above all, how could she have allowed herself to love Luke Scott?

CHAPTER SEVEN

LUKE stayed away for two weeks, during which time Maria had convinced herself that she was unlikely ever to see him again without actively seeking him out, so she could only stare incredulously for several seconds when she opened her apartment door in response to the bell's summons early on a Friday evening and found him standing there.

There was a slight tremor to the hand she had raised, as if she could hold off the madness that way, and she dropped it swiftly as she absorbed the hardness of his saturnine face and the overt demand glittering hotly in his eyes.

'Wasn't once enough for you, Luke?' The tone was blistering, but her smile was twisted and her heart knocked painfully behind her ribs, its pace unhealthy.

'No,' he answered her curtly. 'Not nearly enough, Maria.'

He was moving into the hallway, and Maria backed away, afraid of her feelings again, terrified of any physical contact between them. She knew what would happen. The craving of her flesh for more of that fighting lovemaking would instantly override all other considerations—pride, her awareness of his contempt, the knowledge that he could destroy her.

Temptation was even more dangerously irresistible now that she knew she loved him. Just the sight of him, his height and the strength she had gauged so intimately, and his darkness, emphasised by the light colours of his casual clothing, provoked the yearning, that molten clamouring throb of hidden flesh, with the anguished clenching of her heart its emotional counterpart.

'Well, it was enough for me. Quite enough—more than enough.'

Recklessly she built up the lie, agitatedly aware that she was protesting too much in her desperation but unable to prevent herself.

'Strange. . . Your mouth stays beautiful when you're lying,' he quipped drily, closing the door and clicking one of the locks.

But the dark grey eyes were smouldering as they dropped briefly from the stormy curve of her mouth to her body, scantily clad in garments that were casual in the extreme, her favourite faded denim shorts cut from an old pair of jeans, and the little white cotton bustier into which she had changed on her return from work, planning to spend the humid twilight time out on her balcony before preparing to attend a local record company's promotion party.

Then Luke returned his attention to her tense face, their eyes meeting, too much knowledge in both pairs.

'For God's sake, Luke, leave me some pride!' The words emerged involuntarily in response to that moment of stark recognition. 'Leave me alone!'

'I can't!' he grated. 'Do you think I don't feel it in my pride too, Maria? I don't enjoy this any more than you do, but it's got us well and truly trapped, hasn't it? I wish to God once had been enough. I thought it might be—that's why I went back to Hong Kong, so I wouldn't be tempted to see you and start believing it wasn't. I didn't want an affair with you—I don't! But if these last couple of weeks are anything to go by, I'm never going to know any peace, never stop burning, never be able to take an interest in anyone until this thing between us has run its course.'

'Aren't you exaggerating? What about Cavell Fielding?' Maria wondered waspishly, and saw Luke's surprise. 'Giles said he and Ursula had been out with the two of you. Does she know that you've been unfaithful to her once already and are willing to be again—except that this time I'm not co-operating? Or are you hoping to keep her in ignorance so you can go back to her when you get tired of me and start wanting to respect yourself again? Has it occurred to you how hypocritical you're being when——?'

'Cavell and I have never been lovers,' Luke interrupted her incisively. 'Yes, I know some people might think we are because we occasionally partner each other, but *you* should have known better—or perhaps not, since you never had any scruples about being a party to another man's infidelity six years ago, which leads me to believe that this show of conscience on Cavell's behalf is just that—show! You don't really have any inhibitions about stealing, do you, Maria? But you won't be, anyway. In fact, you were the first woman I'd made love to in quite a long time, and I haven't even been interested in anyone since you were offered this job here and accepted it. I was waiting for you. . .and then after that night I was here with you, I tried to convince myself that it was over, that I didn't need any more. But it's not ended yet, is it? You're in my blood. These past two weeks. . . Have they been as bad for you, darling?'

Maria was momentarily gripped by an odd, angry despair in response to his denial that he was having an affair with Cavell. Resistance might have been easier if he had been, not that her belief that he was had been enough to stop her succumbing to him once. Shame swept through her.

She was still digesting the resentment with which his concluding confession was coloured and the mockery lacing his final endearment as Luke reached for her.

Inevitably, resistance melted the moment he touched her.

'Yes! I was lying. . . Oh, God, Luke! I want you,' she confided passionately, arching against him and repeating it urgently. 'I want you!'

This time he didn't make her wait, because he couldn't. They didn't even get as far as the bedroom, one of the soft rugs strewn over the carpeting in her lounge serving as their bed of reunion, Maria still partly and Luke almost fully clothed as they subsided on to its subtly glowing colours.

Maria was sobbing with desire as she felt his hands push insistently at her thighs, and then the rigid flesh she had freed to her caress just moments previously was nudging at her body, demanding entry and release. She welcomed the welding of hot flesh with a harsh gasp, rent by searing pleasure as the powerful rhythm of his thrusts rocked her. She kneaded at his chest in an agony of rapture before clinging, nails biting into him as he drove deeper, striking into the heart of her desire with a passion that convulsed them both and hurtled them to a zenith of sensation stunning in its ferocity.

'Oh, God, Maria!' Luke groaned as she fell back.

Spent, his lower body still made one last involuntary thrusting movement like a reminder or a promise of more, and then he was withdrawing, moving away from her immediately, levering himself to his feet and standing with his back to her.

Maria looked at him in silence for a while, and when she could breathe easily again and felt she had the strength, she rose.

'Is that how little regard you have for me?' she asked bitterly. 'Unprotected sex, since you don't even know if I'm using anything myself——'

'It's how much I wanted you.' Luke's tone was equally bitter, and he kept his back to her.

Without another word, Maria left the room.

She showered, struggling not to weep, and slipped on her emerald robe before returning to the lounge. Luke was standing outside on the balcony, and once again she found herself looking at his back.

This was the true defeat, she knew. Once might be excusable, but twice, and all the other times to come——

A wave of shamed heat engulfed her. She had sold pride for pleasure.

But she loved him, and that made it a bargain—and he didn't even deserve to be loved.

The thought provoked anger, imparting brittleness to the statement she addressed to his back.

'I have to go out this evening.'

Luke turned to face her, shadow making a mystery of his expression.

'Cancel whatever it is,' he advised her.

'It's work-related.'

'Important?'

'Oh, I suppose if you're offering me a position as your wife—consort—in Hong Kong, anything to do with my career here can easily be sacrificed,' she taunted.

'Don't be ridiculous!' Rejection, unsoftened by any hint of humour.

'No, I didn't really think you were.' Flatly.

'What is the occasion?' asked Luke.

'A couple of the DJs and I have been invited to a party being given by one of the local music companies. They're all wooing us now that we're playing local music, wanting to introduce us to their artists, sampling us with their product.'

'Is Jones one of the jocks?'

'No, two of our Mandarin-speaking contingent. My assistant Penny is also going.' Maria paused. 'Do you want to come with me?'

'No, but if you'll give me your spare keys I can be waiting here for you when you get back. I must collect my gear and check out of the hotel. . . I suppose you do realise that I'm planning to stay for the weekend?' Luke added mockingly. 'I'd make it longer, but I have to be back in Hong Kong on Monday. Are you likely to be late?'

'No.'

So this was how it was going to be from now on, Maria accepted as she turned to go and find the keys. Now that Luke had her, now that he knew she was incapable of resisting him, there was no longer any need for him to be seen with her. Theirs was going to be a secret affair.

'What's wrong?' Luke had followed her into the lounge.

'Nothing.' She extracted her spare set of keys from the pretty jar of locally made pottery she had bought when Nicky Kai had taken her to visit an unusual pottery one day. 'But I'd like to *talk* to you when I get back. I'm running late.'

He grinned slightly at the emphasis, but grew serious again at once.

'Then I'll leave you to get ready. But there is one thing that needs to be said now. If you're *not* already using some form of contraceptive, you'd better see to it, although normally I'd agree that it's a joint responsibility, since it seems that I'm so atrociously lacking in control where you're concerned. . .damn you, Maria.'

The last three words were uttered under his breath and he looked as if he hated her, she saw, made fully aware of his resentment.

'And damn you, Luke. I know just how you feel,' she returned with violent mockery before turning away.

There were things to be said and asked, things they both needed to understand, but she wasn't inclined to risk such a potentially traumatic discussion now, so shortly before she had to go out and be both professional and sociable. Her mood was already hyper-emotional as it was.

Over the next few hours, she thought she was succeeding in calming herself, but the superficial serenity proved fragile, shattering when she got home and found Luke comfortably ensconced in her lounge with a newspaper and some overtly erotic instrumental music playing softly in the background.

It was the implications of his presence as much as the sight of him that heated her skin and caused her heart to thunder as her mind leapt treacherously forward to the night that lay ahead of them.

'Have you eaten?' he asked as he rose.

'Yes.' She remembered a handful of snacks consumed without appetite. 'You?'

'Yes, at the hotel. Come and sit down,' he invited her, indicating the elegant stone-coloured couch he had been occupying.

Maria hesitated, self-consciously aware of the stupidity of resistance now when their relationship was a *fait accompli* and irreversible, but disturbed by the way he was regarding her. The sensual appraisal was mixed with a hint of amusement which could have been in response to her apparent coyness, or perhaps her short-skirted dress with its modest round neckline was the cause, its clash of riotous colours outrageous, orange running into scarlet into crimson with small touches of hot pink.

'I have to ask you some things,' she cautioned him

tightly, finally stepping round the coffee-table and seating herself.

'Yes?' he prompted, sitting down again.

'Are we. . . Is this an affair?' It sounded gauche, and she felt a prick of resentment, hating the way he could reduce her to this humiliating state of uncertainty.

'I can't think what else we should call it,' Luke returned sardonically. 'Can you?'

'Oh, I can think of several things,' she told him with soft-voiced hostility.

Impatience tightened his face. 'If you're going to start fighting this all over again, denying——'

'I'm not fighting anything,' Maria cut in bitterly. 'I can't, can I? You used the right word earlier—trapped. No, I'm just seeking answers. I want to know exactly where I stand. For instance, how long is it going to last, Luke?'

He shrugged irritably, a trace of resentment evident in his manner. 'How the hell should I know? As long as it takes for us to tire of each other, I suppose. As long as it lasts.'

Her dark eyelashes screened her eyes momentarily. 'And what happens if it lasts longer for one of us than it does for the other?'

The challenge clearly didn't appeal to Luke and he was silent for several seconds, contemplating it distastefully.

'Do you really think that's likely?' he countered eventually. 'When we're so perfectly matched, the duration is likely to suit us equally perfectly. It began at the same time for both of us, didn't it? The moment we set eyes on each other. . .six years ago.'

Maria recognised the evasion, but she was disinclined to challenge it. She knew the answer anyway. For her, this would last a lifetime, because she loved him. Luke would tire of her, and the answer to her original question already lay like a shadow on her mind. She would be left—bereft.

'Next question,' she moved on with wan humour. 'How often am I likely to see you?'

The look he gave her was angry and he stirred restlessly.

'What is this?' he demanded.

'At a rough guess?' she persisted tartly. 'If I'm going to have to organise my life around flying visits from you, I'll need to have some idea.'

Luke expelled a harsh sigh. 'All right, then. Weekends, when I can get away, I suppose. I can't be more accurate than that.'

Maria inclined her head, a sharply mocking smile curving her mouth as she assessed the role she was to occupy in his life. Pride protested, but love and desire were paramount.

'How convenient that we live and work in different countries!' she taunted waspishly, disinclined to make his victory too sweet, total though they both knew it was. 'This really has worked out perfectly, hasn't it? Just the way you once wished it could when you were regretting the good old days when a man could keep his unsuitable mistress hidden away, knowing she'd be there waiting upon his pleasure, whenever he felt the urge and could spare the time to see her. Of course, in those days the mistress was generally kept by her lover, set up in a cosy little love-nest somewhere, her accounts settled with no questions asked. . . Although I suppose we could say that you're supporting me, since you employ me, but, unlike the gentleman cads of those sepia-tinted days, you might find you occasionally have to take second place to the demands of your mistress's work!'

She hadn't realised how much it angered her until she had begun, and by the time she came to a halt, her voice had acquired all the sting of a whiplash. Luke had no right to be ashamed of her!

'May I remind you that you will *frequently* have to take second place to the demands of my work?' His own tone was silken but deadly. 'No, we're going to be modern lovers, Maria, our respective careers the primary reason for a certain unavoidable number of solitary nights. But if the arrangement doesn't suit you, we'll have to think of something else.'

He would make the arrogant assumption that she was complaining about all the times separation would deprive her of him. The solitary *nights*, because that was the only way he wanted to consort with her—in bed. She was to be his private partner only, kept from public knowledge.

'Oh, but it suits me perfectly, Luke,' she disabused him of the conceit with a blistering smile. 'You see, I'm just as ashamed of all this as you are.'

Except that it would embarrass him if it were known that he was involved with someone like her, whereas she was ashamed of herself. Was she really prepared to accept all this humiliation for the sake of however many weekends he spared her before he tired of her? Bleakly she wondered what sort of person she would have become by the time that happened.

Luke's face had darkened, but he only said dismissively, 'I think we understand each other perfectly, then.'

'I hope so.' Still an urge to hit out compelled her, a need to try and hurt him in retaliation for the pain he dealt her with his unhidden contempt. 'But in case you need it spelt out, I'm just as anxious as you are to keep this shameful secret of ours hidden. I don't think I want my friends and colleagues here knowing about this.'

It wasn't true. She didn't care one way or the other,

but the moody glance he sent her provided a small measure of compensation for all the insults she had endured from him.

'As you wish, although you can hardly imagine that Jones would mind if he did find out. I doubt if exclusivity in a relationship is something he values,' Luke taunted inimically. 'Or does the famous double standard apply here? He can indulge himself with whichever other women attract him, but you're to remain for his exclusive use, keeping yourself unencumbered, ready and available for whenever he has a whim to renew the relationship?'

'The same way you expect me to keep myself for your use now,' Maria snapped derisively, scalded by the shame of the knowledge that that was exactly what she was going to do, and tired of hearing about her supposed affair with Florian. 'For the last time, I am not involved with Florian Jones, and I don't want to be.'

'Keep it that way, then,' he advised her. 'If only until this is over. I don't share.'

As he spoke, he reached out for the hand that was nearest to him, uncurling her fingers from the tense fist they had formed without any difficulty as the contact had its inevitable effect on her. Despair swamped her. What was the point of fighting him with words when she was utterly incapable of doing so physically?

Already, as Luke raised her hand to his mouth, response was quivering to life deep down in the heart of her femininity, flickering and then leaping as she felt the sensual brush of his lips.

Helplessly she gazed at him, seeing how his pupils dilated as awareness flared, her own eyes darkening as a shivering sigh escaped her.

'Just don't ever forget that I hate you, Luke,' she reminded him in a fine, tense little voice, staving off

complete sensual surrender for a few desperate
seconds.

But the hatred was merely the other side of love, the
element that darkened it, touching their passion with
the hostility that made their lovemaking resemble
fighting.

Self-hatred was the purer emotion.

Luke lifted his lips from her hand briefly, giving her
a hard smile.

'It doesn't seem to matter, though, does it?'

It was so contemptuously dismissive that Maria
recoiled, but only momentarily, the flame of desire
already burning too hot and high to be denied.

Later that night, when they had spent their passion
lavishly once already, only to find themselves caught in
its thrall again an amazingly short while later, anguish
tore at her.

Luke *ought* to love her. So much passion ought to
stem from something much more than lust, especially
when the man it held in its toils was one of Luke's
calibre. Civilised men, possessed of considerable intellect, as he was, could generally control their lust and
even deny it when it was felt in response to a woman
who was either despised or prevented from reciprocat-
ing for a variety of reasons, but they could not always
control their emotions.

And yet, despising her, Luke couldn't resist her any
more than she could him—but she alone had love to
justify the weakness.

Luke didn't love her. It had hurt almost unbearably
earlier, when he had withdrawn from her to lie turned
away from her once more, the shoulder he presented
to her as eloquent a rejection as his disinclination to
touch her.

Now he was touching her again, but only because
desire had renewed itself, and she was helpless in the

grip of a wild excitement once more as she felt the erotic plunge of his tongue filling her mouth and a tormenting finger drew sensual circles round her navel.

How much could she endure? In the act of sliding a hand lovingly up over the satin-smooth skin stretched over the hard muscles of his upper arm, Maria halted as fear of the future caught at her and her fingers dug violently into his flesh.

Luke freed her mouth. 'What's wrong?'

She couldn't see his face clearly in the darkness, only the gleam of his eyes.

'I was just wondering how much I'm really going to enjoy being a sex slave,' she told him bitterly, panting slightly as his hand moved lower, his palm flattening itself against her stomach.

'It's both of us, my darling,' he retorted, the mockery harsh. 'Can you doubt it? This has got us both imprisoned, me as much as you.'

'Passion's prisoners,' she offered with acid amusement but none of the simple pleasure she usually took in alliteration.

Luke's hand moved on, his light fingertip locating the tiny peak of sensitivity which he already knew to be utterly vulnerable to his skills, and Maria moaned softly as a pang of piercingly erotic sensation went thrilling through her.

'As for enjoyment,' he went on tauntingly, his breath mingling with hers as he bent his head again, 'tell me you're not enjoying this, Maria.'

'And you'll call me a liar,' she muttered feverishly. 'You know I am. Damn you, Luke!'

'And you, my darling.'

Then she was giving him her mouth again so that he might swallow the choked cries of pleasure rising from her throat as the frenzy claimed her once more, and a little later she was thrashing against him, pleading hoarsely for his possession, until Luke held her down and sank into her with a harsh groan.

And when the frantic, plunging ride was over, ecstasy a fading quiver of memory and her swollen lips no longer muttering his name over and over in a delirium of rapture, he broke her heart all over again by moving right away from her, the distance between them, now that passion was spent once more, saying everything about their relationship.

So their affair was begun, their part-time affair, as Maria took to calling it, at first only to herself, but then aloud in Luke's presence when she discovered that it could bring a quick frown to his face. She loathed herself for such pettiness, but she was so helplessly without any control over their relationship that pride or all that remained of it demanded that she administer these little pricks to his satisfaction, although she knew she had no hope of succeeding in puncturing it properly.

Theirs was not a loving affair; although she loved him, Maria refused to show it, knowing that Luke would probably reject any attempt to do so anyway. He had his victory already as it was, complete and undeniable. He didn't deserve anything more from her, and certainly not the opportunity to draw derisive satisfaction from the fate that had befallen her.

He came to her on Friday evenings, departing again in the early hours of Monday morning, and the nights they spent together were frenzied.

'Our orgies,' Maria called them once. 'Friday nights because we haven't been together for four nights, Sundays because we know there are another four ahead of us, and. . .why Saturdays?'

'Because that's the way it is with us,' he returned with the faintest of smiles. 'Do you think it would be different if we had the opportunity to be together every night?'

'I don't know.' She paused. 'Do you?'

Luke took a moment or two before admitting, 'I don't know either.'

'Where do you live in Hong Kong?'

It was late on a Sunday morning and they were still in bed, the radio on but turned down low. The glance Luke gave her was suspicious.

'I have a house near Repulse Bay,' he told her, sounding reluctant.

'And your mother?' Surprise silenced her for a moment. 'I've just realised! I don't know if you have any other family. Brothers and sisters?'

'What is this?' Seeing her blank look, Luke elaborated, 'This polite getting-to-know-you line of questioning?'

Maria sat up, eyes changing from warm honey to pure sparkling gold as anger surfaced.

'Just that. Getting to know you, Luke,' she snapped.

'You know all you need to know,' he countered dismissively.

'Sorry, I'd forgotten! There's only one area of your life you want to share with me,' she recalled caustically, getting out of bed and reaching for her robe. 'Except that we can't spend every minute of the time we're together making love, can we? You give a good impression of being Superman, but you're not really, and I'm definitely not Superwoman. So what do you suggest we do when we're not making love or asleep? Sit around in silence like strangers?'

'Oh, for God's sake, aren't you overreacting? But then so was I, probably,' Luke added, surprising her. 'Come back to bed.'

But Maria wasn't ready to forgive him. 'I'm going to

shower. What sort of breakfast do you want? Or we could go out for it.'

The suggestion was casually made, but sheer masochism had prompted it. She knew exactly what Luke's response would be.

'No, we'll have it here. I'll get it, though.'

Maria paused at the bathroom door, her eyes shadowed as she looked back at him, her lover—who was ashamed of being her lover. Except for occasional—rare—meals at a nearby restaurant, they never went out, sending out for meals when they didn't feel like cooking, while Luke no longer even accompanied her to the various work-connected functions she sometimes had to attend at weekends, dealing with business matters of his own or else remaining at the apartment while she was out.

'Aren't you afraid I'll try to blackmail you when this is over?' she enquired sweetly.

'Perhaps it will never be over.'

Still apparently relaxed, hands clasped behind his head, Luke spoke lazily, but his eyes were intent as they probed her taut face.

'Or sell my story to some Hong Kong newspaper?' Maria swept on tauntingly. 'You're famous all over the Far East, so a story about how you kept a secret concubine in Taipei should be worth quite a bit.'

'Except that you'd never expose yourself like that.' Expression and voice had both hardened. 'You're too ashamed of your own contribution to our relationship.'

'Fortunately for you,' she agreed swiftly, having momentarily forgotten that she had deliberately given him the impression that she wanted their affair kept secret.

'What's this all about, Maria?' Luke went on, his tone grown insolent. 'You're the one who views our affair in all these anachronistic terms. Concubine. . .

My God! So what's the problem? All this empty talk
of blackmail, and selling your story when it's over—
are you talking around the real issue here, some
present shortcoming? Perhaps I'm interpreting my role
incorrectly. Am I supposed to be showering you with
gifts right now, pretty things, baubles you can——?'

'No, damn it, Luke!' Maria cut him short, her face
flaming. 'Don't add acquisitiveness to the long list of
my sins. It's not true and you——'

Afraid she was going to cry, she whirled round
without finishing it, going into the bathroom and
slamming the door. She did cry a little, almost sound-
lessly, and was furious with herself for doing so, her
tears mingling with the spray of the shower.

It wasn't his words that had hurt, but the intention
behind them. Maria didn't think Luke seriously
believed she craved some material gain to show for
their relationship. He had meant to hurt and humiliate,
that was all.

She washed her face a second time after stepping out
of the shower and left the bathroom confident that no
trace of her weeping was visible. Luke had left the
bedroom, and after putting on denim shorts and a little
broderie anglaise top, she found him outside on her
balcony, with the bamboo table she had recently purchased with four matching chairs set for breakfast, the
muesli-type cereal he knew she always ate put out for
her along with yoghurt, fruit juice and coffee.

From a domestic point of view, she found Luke easy
to live with, tolerant of delays and minor disasters, and
willing to undertake a fair share of the cooking and
other tasks without comment or the expectation of
praise and thanks.

He had pulled on jeans but nothing else, and his
shirtless state, bare feet and the fact that he had yet to
shave gave him a vaguely disreputable appearance.

Maria paused, looking at him and loving him so much it hurt.

To counteract the feeling, she said waspishly, 'So where's my diamond necklace?'

He gave her a faint, wry smile of acknowledgement. 'You know damned well I was only talking. Whatever the problem is, it's not the frustration of any mercenary instincts, because you aren't excessively materialistic.'

'There's no problem—no new problem,' she amended moodily, seating herself. 'Maybe it's just natural rot setting in.'

'Maybe,' he agreed, helping himself to coffee, the look he sent her slightly wary. 'What do you want to do today?'

'I don't know. Loaf around. . . I still haven't found time to take a proper walk over there,' she added, indicating the expanse of formal parkland stretching out below them.

'Then we'll make time,' Luke offered expressionlessly.

'No one we know is likely to see us,' she added mockingly, conveniently forgetting that Florian and Nicky's balcony a floor up commanded an almost identical view.

She let her eyes roam. It was late August now and Taipei remained intensely hot, a city set in a bowl ringed with mountains, hence its oppressive humidity. The parkland and the distant country were beautifully green, but, as was usually the case, the sky was obscured by a covering of cloud which hid the sun but did nothing to lessen its heat.

Later, as they strolled on neat walkways and over pretty Oriental stone bridges, Luke's mood grew more relaxed, so Maria reintroduced the subject which had been the initial cause of their earlier conflict.

'Are you an only child?' she asked.

He was immediately wary again. 'Yes.'

'And you grew up in Hong Kong?' she persisted, refusing to be deterred.

'Yes. Maria——'

'Why are you so defensive about that side of your life?' she cut in, a perverse urge to torment him rising in response to the warning note in his voice and the rejection hardening his face. 'Your family? Or are you just being protective? I can't harm them—the way you once harmed my family when you only meant to harm me! I've noticed it before. Your expression goes. . .it closes, especially if I mention your father and his dying. . .oh, God, did something terrible happen to him, Luke?'

'Nothing,' he answered her belatedly contrite question curtly, but then something seemed to snap and his eyes blazed. 'Other than dying, nothing more terrible than one of your kind getting her claws into him and then refusing to let go over all the years he spent struggling to free himself.'

'Your. . .no,' she realised. 'He had an affair?'

'Just the one, but it was renewed periodically over the years because the bitch was irresistible, and she knew it.'

It explained his reaction to her supposed affair with Florian. Maria's heart clenched as she slanted a look at his grim countenance.

'And you and your mother knew about it?' she prompted.

'No, for some reason I didn't. When I was younger, probably simply because of that widespread reluctance to believe that one's parents have sex lives of any sort, and as I grew older, because I didn't see that much of them except socially.' Luke paused and she sensed his reluctance to continue. 'Oh, I knew theirs wasn't an entirely happy marriage, that there were quarrels, but it didn't occur to me that the cause lay outside the marriage. It was only after he went into hospital that I started spending much time with him, because we knew his illness would run a rapid course. He told me then, I don't know why, but pain and drugs usually have a lot to do with that urge to confess that seems to overtake the dying. I've never mentioned it to my mother. I think she's suffered enough humiliation without having to endure the knowledge that her son is aware of it. She went to live back in Britain soon after he died, anyway.'

Maria was aware of a fatal softening somewhere within her, and she knew she was in danger of forgiving him—everything. The facts made the contempt he had felt for her, six years ago at any rate, even more understandable. He had come straight from receiving a shock like that to find another woman apparently destroying another marriage, probably because he was half expecting her to do so at that stage, viewing all women with newly disillusioned and suspicious eyes. He couldn't have reacted with anything other than disgust.

Then!

'Aren't you taking rather a one-sided view of it?' she ventured sharply. 'There could have been lacks in the marriage that you weren't aware of, that made him——'

'Who are you really trying to make excuses for, Maria?' Luke cut her short, his tone savagely contemptuous. 'Just my father, or unfaithful husbands in general—or Florian Jones? At least my father tried to get out of the trap, but I doubt if Jones has ever struggled, even with his conscience. Oh yes, there probably were lacks or flaws in the marriage, as in most marriages. The person for whom there's no excuse is——'

'Me, because in your eyes your father's mistress and I are one and the same,' Maria inserted acidly.

'A type, anyway,' he conceded drily.

'Then let me make excuses for *her*!' she flared. 'Perhaps she loved your father.'

'You should know,' Luke allowed derisively.

'I should have realised that you had a *personal* prejudice,' she taunted.

'And I should have realised that you'd be the one who could only see the thing from one angle,' he retorted harshly. 'So let's drop it, Maria.'

'So you can keep on cherishing your prejudice?'

'I said drop it, Maria,' Luke repeated tightly, his anger barely controlled. 'In view of your attitude, I assume you were the child of a happy marriage?'

'I was denied the chance to listen to any deathbed confessions! Otherwise—you'll probably hate hearing this—we've got something in common, Luke!' The mockery was blistering. 'I'm also an only child and my mother, who's very English, also went home to her own folk after my father died in South Africa.'

'What happened?'

'It was emphysema-related.'

Now Luke was looking at her speculatively. 'And you weren't there.'

'I wasn't there,' Maria confirmed, but she found she was having to force the resentment now, needing to remind herself—and him—of all the other lesser things she had lost as well. 'I also had to give up my part-time Communications course which the Jo'burg job was paying for, because the salary in Durban was much lower and my parents couldn't help me when it was all they could do to meet Dad's medical expenses, since he never made any sort of provision for the future. He was one of those people who only care about the present moment.'

'And you hate me for all that, of course,' Luke accepted neutrally.

'I used to. I thought I did. I was wrong.' Abruptly she let go of the last protective remnants of self-deception, but, fearing questions she couldn't answer without exposing the full extent of her vulnerability, she rushed on, 'I felt guilty to begin with, but I did come to terms with it eventually, and anyway, my parents had encouraged me to stay with radio even though it would take me away from them and they knew what was happening to Dad.'

Luke didn't pursue it, but he wore a slightly grim expression as they walked on in silence.

Her hatred—if it had even been that—had turned out to be as intensely personal as her love and an intrinsic part of it, Maria acknowledged privately. It had been born of an instinctive recognition of the damage he could do to her emotional independence and, paradoxically, exacerbated by the way he had deprived her of himself by having her dismissed from that job; finally there had been his open contempt when they had met again. . .

She felt depressed, suspecting that her quip about rot setting in had held more than a few grains of truth. Relationships were difficult things, to be worked at, and how could any survive when the love in it came from one side only? An end was inevitable.

But not yet, please!

CHAPTER EIGHT

'I DON'T know how much longer we can hope to keep this a clandestine relationship,' Luke said sardonically one Friday night when the immediate edge of the savage hunger for each other that built up during their partings had been soothed by a wildly abandoned reunion. 'Jones and Nicky Kai were leaving the building when I arrived this evening, and as Jones seemed to imagine that I was here to call on him I simply explained that you were the object of my presence.'

'The sex object,' quipped Maria, a sweet clenching sensation assailing her loins as she reflected on the helplessness of her response to his torrid lovemaking, resentment rising a second later because she still lacked any semblance of control over their relationship. 'I don't think you need to worry, Luke. Florian is too unimaginative to make anything of it. He probably just assumed that you were seeing me in connection with my work.'

'You could always lie to that effect if he does happen to ask you about it,' Luke suggested harshly.

She stiffened beside him in the darkness, absorbing the bitter truth. Luke was still so ashamed of wanting her, of his inability to deny himself, that he couldn't bear the thought of anyone, even someone like Florian, for whom he had absolutely no respect, knowing about their affair.

'I've told you, he won't. He's too self-centred,' she snapped. 'The world revolves around Florian, and anything that doesn't involve him doesn't interest him

for long either. The only people he really feels any
curiosity about are his listeners——'

'Do we have to have him here in bed with us?' Luke
interrupted, shifting irritably.

'You introduced the subject,' Maria defended herself
angrily.

'I mentioned meeting him,' he corrected her
impatiently. 'But an in-depth analysis of the man's
character is the last thing I want, and damned tasteless
in the circumstances.'

'But what are the circumstances?' she challenged
tauntingly.

'Right now you're in bed with me, Maria, not with
Florian Jones,' he reminded her cuttingly.

Furious, she sat up. 'I wish to God I wasn't!'

'Tell me to leave, then.'

He had been lying on his back, some distance away
from her as usual, but as he spoke he turned on to his
side, reaching out and laying a hand lightly across the
smoothness of one slender thigh. Humiliated, Maria
felt her nipples grow instantly turgid and experienced
again that inner sensation of warmth and weakness.
The breath she drew sounded like a sob.

'You know I can't, damn you,' she conceded
anguishedly, appalled by her vulnerability as he drew
her down into his arms. 'And I hate it! I hate the way
you control this whole thing. . .and now you're even
demanding control over the subjects we talk about!'

'We can talk about anything you please,' he dismissed the protest indifferently, but then the hand that
had slid up to her hip tightened possessively. 'Only
Jones is banned. I won't have him here in bed with us.'

Later, when they lay quiet and apart once more,
Maria thought about his attitude, adding it to the oddly
driven way in which he had just made love to her. He
had been fiercely possessive, racked by an agony of

passionate wanting and yet somehow retaining sufficient control to assert his mastery, denying her fulfilment, waiting until she was almost weeping with desire, as if he needed to hear her husky throbbing pleas confirming his dominion in the relationship.

He was jealous of Florian, she accepted, but she could take little comfort or encouragement from the knowledge, except in so far as it meant that he wasn't ready to put an end to their affair quite yet.

It was only sexual jealousy that he felt, after all, because he had convinced himself that she and Florian had been lovers and probably would be again when this was over. It was a common enough phenomenon, an atavistic instinct with little connection to real emotion.

Nevertheless, it awoke an unexpected flood of tenderness towards him in her, because it made him so very human, this man of whom she had once been so deeply in awe and whose power over her still unnerved her when she reflected on the realities of their relationship.

Inevitably, Luke was lying turned away from her. Immobile, the shape of him was just discernible in the darkness of the bedroom. With the slightest of sighs, Maria put out a hand, her fingers still loosely curled into her palm. The sheet was pulled up only as far as his hip, so that backs of her fingers touched his bare back, warm and still slightly damp.

She had thought he was asleep, realising that he wasn't only when she felt him tense under the light touch of her fingers, but as he neither moved away nor said a word, she let them remain there, resting lightly against him, the contact lax and undemanding.

After half a minute, however, the tenderness still engulfing her compelled her to move closer, the satin softness of her curls slithering across his skin as she touched him gently with her lips, touch becoming kiss as a wave of simple love for him washed through her.

The passionless but overwhelmingly tender and adoring tribute turned Luke's tension to absolute rigidity.

'Cut it out, Maria,' he ordered her curtly after a few seconds in which he seemed to hold his breath.

She recoiled from the blatant rejection in his voice, snatching hand and mouth away and flinging herself angrily on to her back. Hot tears made her eyes smart, infuriating her still further, and she took a moment or two to try and control a surge of pure emotional misery.

'It's the same thing again, isn't it? You have to be in control of everything that's between us,' she accused him defiantly. 'I have some rights here too, Luke. I can touch you if I want to.'

'Not——' He broke off abruptly.

'You touch me whenever you feel like it,' she swept on resentfully.

'Only when I want to make love to you, and that isn't what you've got in mind right now, is it?'

'I wanted to be close,' Maria asserted shakily, uncaring in her agony of how much she revealed.

'I can't!' he grated harshly.

'Don't you——?' She couldn't continue.

'No. You ask too much. Don't!'

She subsided wordlessly, wondering ironically how many times it was possible for the same heart to break before there was nothing left of it. At least when that happened, she would stop feeling his rejection so poignantly—stop caring about the fact that she disgusted him so much that he didn't want anything to do with her except sexually, and that against his will and to the damage of his self-respect.

He didn't want to be close—to her.

Self-respect. Pride. They were things both of them

had sacrificed to this relationship which she was beginning to understand was destructive to both of them.

Perhaps it was her own pride reawakening after all these weeks which prompted her to defy Luke's distaste, albeit only after she was sure he was asleep, moving up close to his back again, lifting an arm and curving it loosely over the side of his body.

Of course, he flung her off when he woke in the morning. Her own sleep the light, fragmented prewaking kind by this time, Maria realised what was happening at once and merely gave him a sleepily complacent smile, pleased to see the disturbance in his eyes as he regarded her suspiciously.

'Yes, all night,' she confirmed tauntingly as realisation tightened his features.

She didn't care, she discovered. She loved Luke, but she didn't care if she had offended him. He deserved it. He had controlled thier relationship for too long, dictating its terms. From now on, she would touch him in any way she pleased, even when neither of them was feeling sexy, because she would still be feeling loving—for as long as the affair lasted.

For the first time, in place of wondering apprehensively when Luke would tire of her, she began to believe that she might be the one to end their liaison, reviving pride rebelling before his lust had faded. It would hurt to do it, to be without him, but she would have to if this went on too long, or he would destroy her emotionally, because she would have nothing left when he did finally tire of her.

But not yet!

Her body was stirring in response to the warmth of his, and Luke was becoming aroused in his turn.

For a moment, as he bent over her, she looked up at him, her parted lips soft and full, and, as had happened in the night, she felt a welter of emotion rising, swamping her heart.

She lifted a hand, touching the hard slope of his dark cheek with gentle fingers, then the arrogant curve of his nose and the darkness of his unshaven jaw.

Recognising the tenderness inherent in the small caresses, Luke looked momentarily distracted. Then his eyes grew hard.

'You expect too much of me, Maria,' he told her tautly. 'I don't. . . . I can't respond to that.'

'I know,' she allowed with a mocking little smile, painfully aware that she could not control what was about to happen but planning more of the same for later, since he found it so unwelcome, her small revenge.

But later that morning Luke was in one of the relaxed moods she was beginning to like so much, helping her move some recently purchased pots and tubs of plants about her balcony, asking questions, laughing at her description of her mongrel ancestry— Irish, Scottish, English, Portuguese and Italian, and intrigued to learn that she spoke Portuguese.

'Oh, it's nothing to do with my single Portuguese ancestor, I'm ashamed to say,' she explained. 'It's just that after we went to live in South Africa it seemed a sensible choice for a third language, as the only non-English-speaking countries among the front line states are Mozambique and Angola.'

'Of course, Taiwan has a Portuguese connection dating back to the days when it was Formosa, but you won't have found any opportunity to air it these days. How fluent are you?' Luke leaned back against the balcony railing, regarding her with bright eyes. 'I have a part interest, about to become sole if negotiations continue as I expect them to, in a tiny Portuguese-language radio station in Macau: Perhaps we should transfer you and utilise your talents there.'

Superficial contentment was stripped away, exposing the raw resentment beneath, because she knew he didn't mean it seriously.

'Isn't Macau a little close to Hong Kong? Think of the potential for embarrassment,' she jeered quietly, playing his game, and meeting his suddenly remote gaze. 'You're never too old to rock'n'roll, as the myth has it, but I've thought I should try something a little more serious than a commercial music station when I move on again. I'm twenty-five now. AIR in Delhi has always attracted radio people from all over the world. All India Radio. There wouldn't be any problem if I was offered a position. I've got two passports, the same as Florian.'

She hadn't intended to introduce Florian's name, and she caught her breath nervously as the unthinking words emerged, but for once Luke didn't react.

'Just remember that your contract commits you to us for two years,' he said coolly.

Maria swallowed, her throat aching.

'But not to you personally, Luke,' she reminded him sharply, turning and walking inside.

It was ten minutes before he followed her, finding her in the kitchen apparently listening to a mid-Saturday morning news flash on the radio there with blank-eyed concentration. He listened to a baseball update and waited for the sponsor's commercial before turning to her.

'What's happening, Maria?' he asked tautly.

'I don't know.' She moved her hands agitatedly, her angry resentment unhidden. 'Maybe. . .maybe it's beginning to. . .wind down now, Luke. Us.'

He was briefly silent, and they both gave a moment's

attention to the incongruity of a particularly poignant song succeeding the somewhat crass commercial.

Then, moving towards her, he said abruptly, 'We've still got this.'

'I don't feel like it,' lied Maria, pushing his hand away from her waist quickly before the madness could rise again. 'I. . . I want to go out for lunch.'

It was a defiant challenge, and he met it with a frown. 'I suppose we could go to the Grand Hotel. No one from the station is likely to be there Saturday lunchtime—too formal.'

The possibility of their affair becoming known to others really haunted him! Maria lifted a hand to hit him, but he looked so grimly reluctant that her fingers had uncurled before they reached his chest, touching him lightly before moving up to the lock of black hair that had fallen over his tanned brow.

As she might have anticipated, Luke stepped away from the gentleness of the gesture immediately, and her face grew as closed as his had suddenly become.

'I'll have to change,' she said flatly, glancing down at her shorts and turning away.

She wished he could love her!

But he didn't. She sometimes wondered if he ever gave her a thought between departing from Taipei early on Monday mornings and his Friday evening returns. He never contacted her during the times they were apart, so perhaps he was able to divorce his professional life from his sex life, compartmentalising them in a way she couldn't. Luke was seldom out of her mind, and the solitary nights she spent were a torment, her bed too big without his presence, the apartment too still and silent.

Somehow, after that, they succeeded in restoring a semblance of what counted as normality in their relationship to the weekend, and it passed without further conflict.

But Maria knew their affair had to end, and soon. If Luke wouldn't or couldn't walk away, she would have to be the one. It couldn't go on. Their mutual dependence was destroying Luke as much as her. No man could go on indulging himself with something he despised and not lose something vital to his integral self.

Taiwan suffered one of its periodic earthquakes early on the Tuesday of the following week, mercifully less severe than many and leaving Taipei itself badly rocked but suffering only superficial damage and few casualties.

However, reports of severe damage and high casualty figures began to come in from communities situated closer to the 'quake's epicentre, and they learned that the emergency services were bringing many of the most badly injured victims in to the capital. Maria made the decision to sacrifice a certain amount of advertising revenue and turn the radio station into a temporary community service, as other stations and television channels were doing, monitoring the situation and providing updates, broadcasting official government warnings and advice to those districts likely to be affected by after-shocks and urging their local listenership to donate blood against a possible depletion of existing supplies.

In the early afternoon she and Florian, with two more of their disc jockeys and a number of other public figures, were variously photographed setting an example, the situation being sufficiently dramatic without being overly traumatic to have induced a general spirit of camaraderie.

That evening, when she was back in her office,

Maria's heart jumped stupidly, betrayed by crazy hope, when Luke walked in.

Then she forced herself to face prosaic reality. She guessed that the earthquake was responsible for his presence, since flights in and out of Taipei were functioning normally again already, but whatever concern had brought him was unlikely to be personal. He was here in his professional capacity, doing the same thing as she was, in essence, as she was planning to remain in the building to offer moral support to any of the staff who might need it, faced with the unaccustomed demands of this minor crisis.

He was merely being a responsible employer.

'Are you all right?' he demanded, and Maria made the shocked discovery that the mere sound of his voice could still make her pulses leap and race, and her heart clench with love and longing.

'We're all fine, there's no damage to the building and we've been able to continue broadcasting without interruption,' she assured him, her voice sharp as resentment rose, and she went on to inform him of the decision she had taken.

'I assumed you'd do something of the sort. The lost revenue will come back to us,' he added cynically. 'This sort of thing can actually work out to a station's ultimate advantage if handled correctly, which it has been, since you've shown us to be flexible and public-spirited. But what about you?'

'What about me?' Maria retorted. 'I think I can cope with any problems that might arise, Mr Scott.'

The lift of his eyebrows was sardonically interrogative. 'Why the formality, Miss McFadden?'

'We're not at the apartment,' she reminded him, bitter mockery curving her mouth. 'Penny is in and out every few minutes at present, and we don't want her to guess that we're more than just owner and programme manager, do we?'

Anger flickered in his eyes. 'I hardly think the use of first names is likely to start her speculating about us.'

'Then how about the way you were so careful to shut the door when you came in?' she challenged wildly.

'I'd have done that anyway, whoever you were,' he returned dismissively, but derision glinted in his eyes as he went on, 'What's worrying you, Maria? I'm not about to risk giving the game away by making love to you here and now. I haven't even kissed you, have I?'

He could hurt her with so little, she reflected, realising that she was finding it more and more difficult to keep hatred alive as a counterbalance to love. It was as if the love had grown too strong lately, absorbing the hatred, and it could swallow her too if she didn't do something about it soon. The hatred had imparted strength of a kind; the love weakened her.

'That would be taking a risk,' she agreed tartly.

'Especially as once we start, we can never confine ourselves to just kissing,' Luke quipped with harsh humour, and paused. 'What time are you likely to be finished here?'

Maria's eyes blazed as she understood what he was asking.

'We have a *weekend* relationship, Luke,' she reminded him pointedly.

'Necessarily, as I can usually only be here at weekends,' he reminded her shortly.

'My life is my own during the week.'

She was compelled by an urge to attempt to hurt him, simply because she herself was hurting, but she was angrily aware that she probably couldn't succeed, because without love, there could be no hurt. At best her rejection could only frustrate him.

Luke's face was shuttered.

'Shared with whom?' he wondered contemptuously.
'Who goes home with you on weekday nights, Maria?
Jones is in the building, isn't he? Is that who you're
waiting for?'

'I'm not waiting for anyone. I'm working—being
here for my jocks and engineers in a crisis situation,
and it may surprise you to know that Florian is also
working.' She was blisteringly angry, but then she
managed to suppress her fury as she remembered that,
while they were here instead of at her apartment, their
relationship was a professional one. 'He's appointed
himself to the temporary monitoring team. He loves a
crisis of this sort, rallying people and so on. It's a
novelty and a distraction.'

'It sounds as if he's bored—restless, then,' Luke
commented tauntingly. 'Doesn't having two women in
his life provide sufficient excitement for him?'

'Professionally, he may be a little restless,' Maria
began, having noticed the signs.

'But personally he's well stimulated and satisfied?'

'Ask him or Nicky Kai—I wouldn't know,' she
flared, shaking her curls back angrily.

'Are——? What's that?'

Luke moved swiftly round the desk to where she sat,
and she flinched as he put out a hand, lifting a loose,
shining curl away from the side of her brow.

'Don't touch me!' she protested agitatedly, distracted
by his sudden proximity.

'What happened?' Luke asked grimly, touching a
slightly sore place on her temple.

'Oh, does it show?' Maria was surprised. 'I couldn't
see anything last time I looked in a mirror.'

'There's a bruise,' he told her curtly, releasing her
hair as she pulled away from him defensively, the inner
disturbance that was her inevitable response to his
lightest touch suddenly infuriating her.

'It's not serious. I bumped it against a door-frame when the earthquake started this morning and I lost my balance.'

'Was it your first earthquake?'

'Yes, although I've experienced severe tremors in other places. This was something else, though.'

Luke studied her in silence for several seconds before saying abruptly, 'Go home, Maria.'

'I can't. I have to——'

'As your boss, I'm ordering you to go home,' he cut her short. 'I'm perfectly capable of dealing with the situation here for you. Does your head ache?'

'A little,' she admitted reluctantly, but it had only just begun to do so, and she suspected that the tension induced by his presence at the end of an unusually demanding day was more responsible than the bump.

'Take a taxi,' he instructed her peremptorily, anger tightening his features as he marked her wary expression. 'Relax, Maria—I'm staying here. As little control as I have where you're concerned, I'm not such an animal that I'd deny you a peaceful night when you're so obviously in need of one. I won't be joining you after all.'

But he would deny her the simple comfort of being a presence in the apartment, she reflected savagely.

'Of course, no sex—no reason for you to join me, right?' she challenged caustically.

'Exactly,' Luke confirmed brutally.

'Aren't you ashamed?' she demanded tempestuously—masochistically too, she realised.

'You know I am.'

'So am I, Luke,' she offered bitingly as she pushed back her chair and rose, wincing as her head throbbed slightly.

His smile of acknowledgement was a travesty. 'I'm not sure if I'll still be here tomorrow, as air traffic is

functioning normally and I have some urgent matters
to attend to back in Hong Kong, but I'll see you on
Friday anyway.'

'If you say so.' Bitterly.

'Oh, I think you also say so, Maria.' Luke was
arrogantly confident. 'We're not nearly done with each
other yet, are we?'

But they had to be, she knew, or the relationship
would destroy them.

She looked at him, loving him. She would tell him
on Friday. This wasn't the time or the place, she
excused her procrastination, guiltily aware of what she
was doing.

'Friday,' she confirmed, and left her office, pausing
to explain to Penny that Luke would be taking over
from her.

He must have left Taipei again later that night or
early the following morning, because there was no sign
of him the next day. The remainder of the week proved
busy, the demands made by the earthquake having
caused a backlog of normal work, in addition to a
sudden need to do something about the restlessness
she had begun to notice in Florian Jones.

She met him emerging from their tall block of
apartments as she was returning from work on the
Friday evening, having stopped to buy groceries on the
way home, her mind flying ahead to Luke's arrival and
all that she planned to say to him now that she had
made up her mind to end their affair.

'Flo! I've been meaning to talk to you, but you've
ducked out of the building so fast after finishing your
show these last two days,' she told him when he
stopped to greet her and ask if she had heard the
brilliant spontaneous earthquake joke he'd cracked on
air that morning. 'You must have a guilty conscience!
Don't worry, it's not the joke, even if it was slightly

sick. It's all over town already—I've heard it twice today. No, this is something I think you'll like.'

'Go and dump your shopping quickly and I'll wait for you at the first bridge,' he suggested, indicating the expanse of parkland their building overlooked.

'I'm not doing any jogging,' Maria warned lightly, cynically inspecting his trainers, trendy running shorts, vest and headband.

'Neither am I,' he retorted, confirming her suspicions. 'I just felt I ought to get out and fill my lungs with some good clean exhaust fumes. I'm looking a bit peaky, don't you think?'

Maria glanced at her watch. It was shortly before the time Luke usually arrived on Fridays, and up until today she would have made some excuse to Florian, but reviviscent pride demanded a gesture. It would prove something to both Luke and herself if for once he didn't find her waiting for him when he came.

Besides, he had keys if he arrived while she was out, so he would wait for her, especially having come all the way from Hong Kong, she comforted herself, with a vague feeling that she was somehow cheating.

'Hawaii!' she announced when she rejoined Florian a few minutes later. 'Three weeks sitting in for the regular breakfast show jock on a commercial station there, while he takes over your show here. The airline we've got to sponsor the exchange is agreeable to the deal including Nicky and the other jock's wife or girlfriend, and obviously the two of you will be expected to take every opportunity to rave on air about what a wonderful flight you had, how royally you were treated and all the rest of it. I worked with the Hawaiian manager for a while once, and we organised a similar scheme for two of our jocks when I was with the Wellington station last year.'

Florian's face had lit up and the questions he started

asking fizzed with enthusiasm, but Maria knew that the exchange would only drive his restlessness into temporary remission, not cure it. Ultimately, the urge to move on that afflicted so many media people, and Florian more severely than most, would demand satisfaction, but she suspected that Luke would be shrewd enough to tempt him with an offer of his choice of all the other stations in which he had an interest. He might not like or respect Florian personally, but he knew he was too good a jock to lose.

'You're brilliant, Maria!' Florian praised her exuberantly as they retraced their steps a little later, having discussed the United States' and Taiwan's regulations and requirements concerning such exchange schemes. 'I've always wanted to go to Hawaii. I'll love it, and the listeners there will love me. I just knew I was inspired when I proposed you for this job here, that it would come back to me in some incredible way. Didn't I tell you we were good together?'

He slapped her on the shoulder and performed a jubilant hip wiggle before leaping ludicrously into the air with a triumphant clenched-fist salute. Her shoulder was stinging, but Maria couldn't help laughing at his effervescent antics.

Treacherous relief replaced amusement and was followed by a great surge of pure excitement as she glanced up at their apartment building. For once she had no need to count up and then across in order to identify her own balcony. Familiar, beloved, Luke's motionless figure had drawn her attention instantly.

'I must get back,' she told Florian, who hadn't looked up.

She heard her own shaming urgency and winced self-consciously, but even if he had been an observant man, Florian was currently too preoccupied to have noticed

it, still busily congratulating himself and probably
fantasising about taking Hawaii by storm.

He gave her an absently unfocused look.

'Me too, I suppose. Yeah, wait until Nicky hears
about this!' he added excitedly, belatedly absorbing the
fact that Nicky was to share the adventure and then
regarding Maria suspiciously. 'Or have you told her
already?'

'Would I spoil your fun like that?' Maria retorted
with a tart smile for his childishness. 'I just hope she's
as pleased as you are.'

'Let's go, then,' Florian urged eagerly, satisfied.

It was typical of his self-absorption that he displayed
no curiosity about her sudden haste to return to her
apartment or her plans for the evening and weekend.
He rarely wondered about others' lives except where
they touched his; his mind was perpetually occupied
with his own concerns.

Just as her own concerns were now absorbing her
fully, the desire to see Luke, to be in his arms again
paramount, the need to end their relationship ignored
for the moment. At this hour, the building's lifts were
all in use, crowded with homecoming tenants, and the
one she and Florian finally entered stopped on every
floor on the way up, prompting a series of grimaces
from an impatient Florian and frustrating Maria
unbearably.

When they reached her floor eventually, she bade
him a perfunctory farewell and stepped out of the lift
with a feeling of release, hurrying towards her apartment, heart and hormones defeating any intention of
greeting Luke's arrival as coolly as if it didn't matter to
her one way or the other.

They met in her lounge, and Maria's tilted smile
faltered and then faded as she saw Luke's expression,
the glittering hostility with which the dark grey eyes

swept the vivid marigold colour of her short tight skirt and her creamy blouse trimmed with hamdmade lace.

'All alone? You haven't brought him back with you, then,' he commented derisively, ignoring the hand she had held out him.

'Who?' Distracted, she let her hand drop. 'Luke——'

'From the ecstatic behaviour I witnessed just now, I thought you must be promising him instant gratification at the very least,' Luke added with savage humour.

'Oh! Florian?' Maria guessed, coldness creeping into her heart.

'Who else, unless you're favouring more than two of us?' he taunted insultingly, his mirthless smile stabbing at her. 'But I don't believe that. It's just Jones, always Jones. . . It never changes, does it?'

'Florian is a colleague!' she flared, trying to contend with the wrenching anguish that rose in response to the sexual jealousy that seemed to mock her with its similarity to the emotional sort.

'Only office hours aren't enough for you, are they?' Luke's lips twisted. 'When it took you so long to get here, I thought you must have gone on up to his place with him, but I suppose Nicky Kai is still in residence. I was really hoping you'd bring him here with you, though, so I could. . . What happened? Did you see me on your balcony and decide you'd have to defer your reunion—if that's what it was going to be? Or are you here to make some pretty excuse that will enable you to see him? Such as a function you have to attend in your professional capacity? How about another music industry bash, for instance? How many times have these affairs been genuine? It was fortunate for you that I never insisted on accompanying you.'

'But think of the embarrassment, Luke!' Maria jeered caustically, driven partly by masochism but also

by a need to lash out as she realised that in addition to
all the other contemptible things he believed of her, he
was now also convinced that she was a liar. 'People
might have guessed I was involved with you.'

Luke's face tightened, but instead of reacting to the
taunt, he pursued his earlier accusation.

'So what's the excuse going to be this time, darling?
Come on, let me hear what you have to say!'

Maria looked at his grim expression and knew what
she had to do. Ashamed of wanting her, ashamed of
having let himself start their affair, Luke was no
happier with it than she was.

'No excuses, Luke, but I have got something to say,'
she told him flatly. 'This has to be the last weekend.
It's over.'

CHAPTER NINE

AFTER a moment, Luke laughed, but there was no real amusement in the sound, and Maria flinched.

'At least you're honest enough to want to end one affair before starting another——' He broke off abruptly, his eyes narrowing as they rested on her tense face. 'Or am I a fool to believe even that much? Has it begun already, Maria? Or I should say, has it been resumed? How much have you been seeing of Jones during the weeks when I've had to leave you alone here? I've never asked before, and until this week I haven't even really wondered——'

'Because you haven't needed to!' Maria inserted tempestuously, suddenly understanding that much quite instinctively. 'You'd have known if I was involved with someone else, the same way I'd have known if you were making love to another woman during the week.'

'Yes, I used to believe that,' Luke conceded slowly, but with no relaxation of his taut features and aggressive stance. 'But now I'm no longer sure what to believe. Perhaps it seems politic to you to end our affair now that you realise you're suspected—found out— whereas it didn't seem to matter while the evidence of your passion in bed could lull me into accepting that there was no one else. I've told you I won't share.'

Maria drew an angry breath. 'I'm ending our affair because I just can't take any more Luke! I can't stand it, what it's doing to us—to both of us. It's a terrible, damaging thing, and it's destroying us as people. We can't like ourselves any more——'

'All this sudden concern for the emotional wellbeing of someone you hate!' Luke was openly sceptical, rejection flickering in his eyes.

'And above all, I'm ending it because I'm tired of being constantly branded a liar,' she asserted emphatically, losing her temper. 'You haven't even asked me directly why I went for a walk with Flo this evening, for instance. No, you've just made assumptions as usual. For what it's worth, I merely took the opportunity to discuss a radio-related matter with him when we happened to meet because I've kept missing him at work these last couple of days. Giles Estwick has got an airline to sponsor one of those international exchange schemes, and Flo is the jock we're sending to this station in Hawaii for three weeks. That's why he was so excited.'

'I don't want to hear this, Maria,' drawled Luke. 'I'm fully prepared to accept that radio forms part of the conversation whenever the two of you get together, as you're both so devoted to it. Perhaps having that in common is partly responsible for what's between you. I don't know about Jones, but you seem to be stupidly sentimental about anything that links you. These newspaper photos you've cut out, for example. Wasn't one enough, or is the second intended for him? Look at the two of you, congratulating yourselves on having just donated blood during Tuesday's emergency!'

Maria had left the identical cuttings anchored by a small china bowl on her coffee-table, but the bowl had been moved, so he must have examined them on arrival.

'I'm not sentimental, and nor am I flattered by having my photo in a newspaper, but my mother likes that sort of thing, so I'm sending one to her in England,' she snapped, and hesitated perceptibly before continuing. 'The other is for Rachel, Flo's wife

in South Africa, because I knew he wouldn't get round
to doing it himself and I thought she'd like to be able
to show their little daughter a picture of her father
doing something responsible and public-spirited for a
change.'

'How touching!' Luke was openly contemptuous.
'She must be a strangely unimaginative or insensitive
woman if she can bear to keep in touch with a woman
who started an affair with her husband when she was
pregnant with their child!'

Maria's eyes blazed. 'Everything always comes back
to sex with you, doesn't it? Every contact I've ever had
with Florian has to have been to do with sex——'

'No, Maria,' Luke interrupted her sardonically. 'Sex
is what you have with me, whereas it's merely one
aspect of your emotional involvement with Florian
Jones. I've always accepted that you're in love with
him, even if you conduct your relationship in a way
most people would find inexplicable.'

'What does it take to convince you?' she demanded
sharply over rising despair, wondering why she was
even bothering to try now that their affair was in its
death throes. 'I am not in love with Florian and I never
have been.'

'Why do you keep on with it, Maria?' Luke
demanded, suddenly wearily contemptuous. 'Have you
forgotten that I know you were involved with him six
years ago? I guessed you were from the first, and the
fact that you could quite happily and openly go away
with him for a weekend everyone would know about
confirmed that I was right. Remember that concert in
Zimbabwe? You felt absolutely no shame, did you?
That's what we really come back to every time.'

Maria was silent, digesting it, slightly incredulous
but forced to accept it at last. Amazingly, that weekend
in Harare all those years ago was the foundation upon

which Luke had built his belief that she was romantically and sexually involved with Florian.

'Can I explain that to you?' she requested quietly. 'I never have before.'

'It explains itself, doesn't it?' Luke countered cynically. 'His wife was unwell back in Johannesburg, but there you were, the other woman——'

'I wasn't a woman then!' Maria protested passionately. 'I was a girl——'

'And you've never grown out of it, have you? No!' The violence of the denial as she attempted to speak again shocked her into silence. 'I don't even want to hear you saying his name again, especially that ridiculous abbreviation you keep using. I can't bear listening to you.'

'Then there's nothing more for either of us to say,' she accepted dully, turning away from him and then halting as the edge of her vision caught the movement he made towards her.

'I would have said we had quite a number of things to discuss, my darling,' Luke contradicted her, the endearment a taunt and a challenge as always, never meant. 'You've just announced the end of our affair, after all.'

'That doesn't require discussion.' Maria was scathing.

'Possibly I used the wrong word. The inadequacies of our language again,' he allowed dismissively. 'But your announcement merits a reciprocal one, Maria. I don't accept it. Yes, I accept that there is this special bond between you and Jones, that he will be first, last and always. I said I accept that. But our affair won't end until desire ends, and, as I said the other night, we've not done with each other yet.'

He was closer now, and Maria's eyes darkened,

becoming the colour of honey in shade as she regarded him apprehensively.

'Don't touch me, Luke,' she warned him in a low, intense voice.

'You still want me,' he claimed softly—arrogantly.

'If you touch me, you rob me of choice,' she said achingly, and swallowed emotionally before adding stormily, 'Damn it, you know that! You know I can't— I can't control what's between us. I never could. You were always the one.'

'If that's the only way—if it's all there is. . .'

As the words died away, Luke shrugged, and Maria saw the light of recklessness leap in his eyes.

She knew what was going to happen. She was so vulnerable to him that part of her was already accepting that defeat was inevitable, that only Luke could be the one to end their affair, but at the same time pride was demanding resistance, refusing to submit to the humiliation of a physical surrender to the man who had called her a liar, accused her of infidelity—the man who had hurt her so badly.

With some wild, unplanned, unfocused idea of shaming him with feminine helplessness, she stayed mute as he drew her into his arms, and remained passive as he gathered her up to him. Then his mouth was covering hers and the hot, fierce thrust of his tongue, plunging deep in shockingly explicit demand, sent a shaft of panic through her.

Finally she fought, trying to escape that devastating possession, twisting her head frantically from side to side until Luke's hands came up to still her struggles.

After that there was nothing she could do, save absorb the impact of the sensual onslaught, and be seduced by it. Luke's mouth pleasured while it dominated, and his hands roaming insolently about her body were creating havoc, the skilled, confident caresses to which he subjected her a bold proclamation of ownership.

Loving and aching, her heart recognised it as such. He was making a statement that was demeaning to her, and yet her flesh burned, familiar fire stabbed at her loins and her body stirred against his, jerkily at first and then involuntarily adopting a rhythm that was both sinuous and surging, blatantly erotic.

'No, we're not ending it yet,' Luke asserted harshly as he raised his head at last, a feverish glitter of triumph in his eyes as she moaned protestingly.

He had released her from his embrace, his hands merely holding her by the upper arms, and she sagged against him, trembling too violently to stand unaided, her knees buckling.

'Luke. . .' His name was barely audible, an anguished sigh, freighted with despair as she conceded defeat once again.

He continued to hold her by the arms for a few seconds longer, studying her face. Then, guiding her, he let her drop to a sitting position on the couch that was behind her.

'You're still mine,' he stated arrogantly. 'For now, and for as long as it lasts. If only in this way. . .'

Abruptly, he knelt in front of her, pulling her forward into his arms again, his mouth falling to plunder the swollen redness of the lips she offered so helplessly.

Passion was consuming them. Maria made a tiny whimpering sound as Luke moved a hand to the tautness of one high breast and then let it drop to rest a moment on her lap. Her skirt had ridden up and she clung to his shoulders convulsively as she yielded to the sweet torment of his long fingers stroking over her thighs.

'Please!' she moaned urgently as he lifted his mouth

from hers to bury his face against the side of her neck,
and excitement leapt as she heard the slight sound of
the zip on his jeans being unfastened.

Devoured by need, she shifted herself instinctively,
anticipating his movement towards her, but it never
came.

'God, no! Ah, no, Maria!' Luke seemed to flinch as
if hurt. 'This isn't the way. I can't——'

He broke off and was still, seemingly frozen, for
several seconds. Then, incredulously, Maria heard the
sound of his zip again.

'Luke——'

Abruptly he jerked away from her, no longer touching her although still kneeling before her with his head
bent.

For a frustrated moment Maria suspected him of
doing it deliberately, to punish her, or perhaps to teach
her some sort of lesson. Then he raised his head, and
she saw his face.

'No!' The word seemed to be torn from him, laden
with reluctant decision, and he flung her a savage look.
'You're right, Maria. This must be the last weekend.'

Her hands ceased their uncertain fluttering, dropping
to her lap as she sat back and then tugging at the hem
of her skirt until it was at a more modest level. She
expelled a shuddering breath.

'Yes!' she concurred emphatically.

A slight ironical smile flickered briefly around Luke's
mouth.

'I suppose your relief is justified,' he conceded drily.

'I couldn't do it,' she explained shakily. 'I knew. . .
I realised just now that you had to be the one to finish
it.'

'Yes. Because, as you've said, I was depriving you of
choice. It wasn't fair to you.' The self-disgust she saw
in his eyes wrung her heart. 'Oh, I might as well tell

you that I've always known I was being unfair to you, using sex to hold on to you.'

'I think neither of us had a choice for a while,' she offered, and he made a slight movement of denial, as if he didn't want to believe it.

'There's no need to emphasise it,' he retorted, resentment clearly audible. 'Or do you think I don't despise myself sufficiently already? Just sex, that's all it was, and yet there I was, prepared to—ah, hell!'

The truth would never lose its power to wound, but Maria lacked any inclination to retaliate, aware that the same truth must be hurting Luke just as deeply, albeit in an entirely different way. It would be a long time before he stopped despising himself for having succumbed to a purely physical attraction, and that towards a woman he despised.

'We were both trapped, you once said,' she reminded him helplessly, with some idea of comforting him, or perhaps easing the process of rationalisation and self-forgiveness he was inevitably going to have to endure. 'Prisoners.'

'And now you're free. Congratulations,' Luke mocked sardonically.

'We both are,' she corrected him gently. 'And I'm grateful to you because, as I've said, you had to be the one to take responsibility for that. I'm also grateful that you didn't. . .you didn't take advantage of what was between us six years ago. You could have—I know that now, and I also know that I couldn't have coped with it then.'

'That's what I suspected at the time, but your damned gratitude is the last thing I want, Maria.' He was angrily dismissive. 'Nor do I want to indulge in a post-mortem—although I suppose it's an appropriate description, if the thing between us is now dead.'

'Quite dead?' Maria questioned him, aware that his

desire for her hadn't died yet even if the need to respect himself again had dictated that he put an end to their affair. 'Can we. . .? We still have this weekend, don't we, Luke? The last weekend.'

'Wouldn't you rather——?' He broke off, regarding her warily for a moment before laughing, a hard, hollow sound accompanied by a shrug that could have been of acceptance, or resignation. 'Yes, we still have this weekend; if you're fool enough to offer, I'm not fool enough to refuse.'

'I'm a fool,' she agreed, saddened by his attitude.

Still he knelt in front of her, and Maria sat forward, lifting a hand and laying it open-palmed against the side of his face for a moment before tracing the angle of his cheek with gentle fingers.

For several seconds Luke remained immobile, scarcely breathing, it seemed. Then he jerked his head away.

'Don't do that,' he instructed her tautly. 'I can't stand it when you touch me like that. It's a travesty—a mockery.'

The brutality of the rejection made her recoil, but she could accept the distaste he felt. Any tenderness between the two of them would be a sham as far as he was concerned, merely serving to emphasise the absence of love, and perhaps like her he felt that a relationship characterised by so much other feeling ought to be loving as well, that the depth of desire he felt for her should have been merely a facet of love instead of the whole.

Anger rose unexpectedly. He should have loved her.

'Like this, then!' she snapped, snatching at him, her mouth seeking his feverishly. 'In case you've forgotten what we were doing a few minutes ago.'

Luke's arms came round her. 'I hadn't forgotten.'

'Make love to me,' she demanded, still angrily, and his hands tightened on her.

'Here, like this? No,' he muttered, rising easily to his feet and pulling her up with him. 'That would have been a mistake. The bedroom.'

Recognising the control he suddenly seemed to have found when she still had none turned her anger to rage. If he had taken her here on the couch a few minutes ago, as he had so nearly done, their abandonment to passion then would have been a mutual—equal— thing, but now he was back to being the dominant partner in what remained of their relationship, control- ling it and her.

It was irrational to be so resentful now when it was so nearly over anyway, but she was too infuriated by his failure to love her to be thinking clearly.

She wanted to be able to hate him again, and she was looking for reasons.

She was violent when they came together in her bedroom a short while later. Forbidden to express her love through tenderness, she compensated with a wild, lavish passion that seemed to draw Luke equally deeply into its extravagant madness. He made love to her with a driving desperation that matched the excesses which were to shock her in retrospect, and if his flesh bore the imprint of her nails and teeth afterwards, there were faint reciprocal marks on her body, mostly the legacy of an erotically suckling mouth.

'I hope I didn't hurt you,' she felt compelled to say politely when Luke had showered and returned to the bedroom.

Surprisingly, his laughter rang with genuine amusement.

'I thought you meant to?'

'You didn't exactly carry on like a pacifist yourself,'

she retorted evasively, mouth reproachful. 'I'm going
to have bruises by tomorrow.'

'They're all you'll have, my darling, so count yourself
lucky,' Luke submitted sharply, his humour abating.

'No baby and no broken heart?' she quipped, hidden
hands clenching, the last a lie.

'Exactly,' he confirmed, so repressively that she was
forced to drop the subject.

They should have guessed that the weekend would
fail them. They were both too conscious that it was the
last, the knowledge weighing heavily on them, giving
rise to complex emotion each time their eyes met, until
eventually they started avoiding looking at each other.

They were also trying too hard, Maria realised quite
soon, and she thought Luke was equally aware of it.
They were trying too hard to make this weekend a
fitting finale to their affair, to match or recapture all
that had gone before—to make a memory to cherish.

They couldn't ignore the fact that they were to part,
and neither of them made any attempt to avoid it in
conversation.

On the Saturday evening, Luke said abruptly, 'This
Hawaiian project, Maria? Are you planning to accompany Jones?'

'No! He doesn't need anyone to tell him how to be a
brilliant jock. He's always worked without a personal
producer.' Halting, she accidentally met his cynical
gaze and was immediately acutely conscious once more
of what he believed of her. 'Nicky will be going with
him.'

Her eyes, threatening to turn from amber to gold as
the two of them sat there over a casual dinner on her
balcony, briefly dared him to develop the theme, just
before she dropped them.

He didn't. Instead he asked mildly, 'You're content

in your job here, aren't you? No plans to try and wriggle out of your contract?'

'No, but. . .' Hesitating, she risked giving him a haunted look. 'Could. . .do you think you could stay away from Taipei for a while, Luke?'

'I think I'm going to have to,' he responded, drenching it in ironical significance, and she winced.

'I'd appreciate it,' she vouchsafed woodenly.

'So you can start practising pretending it never happened,' he derided, fleetingly aggressive. 'It happened, Maria.'

'It happened, and now it's over,' she concurred lifelessly.

'And neither of us is handling it very well,' he added, matching her flat tone.

'Why should I want to remember?' Irritably, she picked up on his previous point. 'Yesterday you were the one who didn't seem to want reminding of. . .of the whole disaster. No post-mortems, you said.'

'What I want and what I'm going to get are two very different things.' Luke paused. 'Are you trying to pick a fight? Quarrels are for lovers.'

Which they no longer were. Luke stopped trying before she did, barely touching her and becoming increasingly uncommunicative. Sheer misery engulfed Maria. She had known their affair had to end or it would destroy them both, but now that it was about to do so, she was terrified of a future in which there would be no Luke, not even Luke causing her unhappiness.

She had been deprived of him once before, six years ago, before she even knew she loved him, and then she had reacted with an endless rage that she had interpreted as hatred. This time, knowing what she was losing and incapable of hating—what was to become of her?

By the Sunday afternoon, she had had enough.

'If you don't want to make love and you don't want
to talk, why don't we go out somewhere?' she suggested defiantly, facing him with her hands on her hips,
a bitter mockery glinting in her eyes. 'After all, it can't
matter if someone who knows us sees us together at
this late stage, Luke. Any speculation would soon be
forgotten or dismissed, because they'll never again see
us together, will they? If they remember, they'll think
they were imagining things, jumping to conclusions.'

Luke looked as if he would like to throw something
at her.

'That really bothers you, doesn't it?' he derided.

'Do you blame me?' Maria countered, quietly
intense.

'No, I don't,' he admitted, surprising her, but then
he lifted a negligent shoulder, dismissing the question.
'So where would you like to go?'

'Somewhere public,' she ventured acidly, 'where we
can look at strangers who organise their lives and
affairs more successfully than we've done.'

'And envy them, or simply remind ourselves that it
can be done? Do you think of us as failures, then?' he
enquired distastefully.

'Aren't we? When we don't like either ourselves or
each other very much? That doesn't sound like success
to me.' It was a bitter summary of their unhappy affair,
but compunction ensued, because it wasn't Luke's fault
that he couldn't love her, even if he had no right to
despise her, so she added neutrally, 'There's a Chinese
tea-house or tea-garden—I'm not sure what it's really
called—not far from here that intrigues me, and I've
been wanting to go and find out what it's all about ever
since I first passed it. We could walk.'

'Anything you say.'

Luke was so infuriatingly indifferent that Maria
almost told him to forget it. But a perverse urge to

take advantage of his rare willingness to be seen out with her made her bite back the words, and she went off to discard her shorts in favour of a slim straight dress, the fine cotton-knit a subtle sage green.

Being out didn't help. A terrible, impersonal courtesy had crept into Luke's manner, and it was breaking Maria's heart all over again. She would even have preferred more of his contemptuous accusations to this present chilling remoteness. At least when he was condemning her he was reacting to her, personally and subjectively; now he was treating her as if she were a stranger.

She could have wept. She was losing him before she had to, with their final parting still hours away, but too soon—too soon!

It was likely to be sooner still, she discovered.

Some time later, when they were walking back and approaching her apartment block, Luke touched her elbow lightly, startling her, since he had been avoiding physical contact with her all day.

'If you don't mind, Maria, I'm going to telephone when we get in and find out if I can get a seat on an earlier flight back to Hong Kong—tonight, preferably,' he added evenly. 'It was a mistake for me to stay after Friday evening. We should have known we couldn't prolong it once we'd agreed that it had to end.'

The light seemed to fade from the brightly shimmering early evening as she heard him, and her heart felt as if an iron band was tightening mercilessly about it.

'Yes, you're probably right,' she agreed tonelessly.

There was nothing else she could say, no protest she could make. She knew it had to end. She had wanted it to.

But she had thought they would still have tonight.

Luke slanted her a sharp glance. 'How badly have I messed up your life?'

Maria gave a dry little laugh as she clamped down on the obvious, defeatist answer.

'It's a question I still have to study,' she offered evasively instead.

'You'll sort it out,' he assured her callously as they entered the building, and she suppressed an urge to hit out at him and tell him exactly what he had done and was doing to her.

'What about you?' she responded in her most creamily civilised voice as he pushed one of the buttons on the panel outside the lifts.

'I'll live with it,' Luke answered somewhat grimly, waiting for her to precede him into an empty lift as the door slid open.

'Hey, hold it, you two!' a familiar voice hailed them from behind. 'Wait for us!'

As Luke automatically put a finger to the button that prevented the door from closing, Maria tensed, turning to see Florian rushing towards them, towing Nicky along by the hand.

She glanced at Luke apprehensively, knowing that he was mature enough to control his dislike of Florian—but probably only as long as Florian refrained from being provocative; if he didn't, and one never knew with Florian, Luke might say or do anything.

Another possibility occurred to her. If Florian or Nicky were to draw the obvious conclusion from the fact that she and Luke were returning to her apartment together, becoming aware of the affair Luke had wanted to keep secret, now when it was ironically no longer an affair——

Maria shivered and, moving closer to Luke to make room for the couple, she touched his wrist lightly with her fingers, unsure if the impulse to do so sprang from an urge to seek reassurance, or to give it.

Luke gave her a slightly surprised look before greeting Nicky and Florian, his manner urbane.

'I wish you'd remember that I haven't got a fast-forward button, Flo!' Nicky was gasping, throwing Maria and Luke a quick apologetic glance and standing on one leg to examine an elegant leather shoe as the door closed. 'I'm sure I've damaged a heel.'

Florian was clearly still floating effortlessly on Friday evening's buoyant mood.

'These women just can't stand the pace, can they?' he appealed to Luke cheerfully before inevitably focusing on his own concerns. 'You've heard about this Hawaiian jaunt of mine, presumably?'

'Maria was telling me,' Luke conceded smoothly.

'Yes, she——'

Florian broke off, looking astonished, and Maria knew him well enough to realise that his attention had made a rare leap outward.

Nicky too must have recognised the uncharacteristic gap in his self-absorption and wondered what was coming, because she rushed into speech.

'He thinks he needs a whole new wardrobe for it,' she giggled. 'I keep telling him people can't see him on the radio.'

But Florian wasn't to be diverted.

'Oh, hey, it's just struck me!' he claimed dramatically, beaming at Maria and Luke. 'The two of you here together on a Sunday, and we met you arriving another time. . . Don't tell me congratulations are due! They are, aren't they? I bet I'm the first to realise! The two of you are. . .how does it go? An item! I just love that phrase—an item. I'm right, aren't I?'

Maria was paralysed, waiting for some sort of explosion, or for Luke to deny that he was involved with someone like her—the truth, *now*.

'Yes.' Utterly expressionless, the word was

addressed to Florian, and she clutched at Luke's hand instinctively, still expecting something more.

Luke glanced at her briefly, but instead of the fury she was anticipating, his expression was complex, more questioning than anything else, and his fingers relaxed, curling themselves about her hand.

Florian was examining her perplexedly.

'I've never got it, this thing about Maria and men—the way she attracts them,' he observed candidly.

'All charm and flattery as usual, Flo,' Maria commented sarcastically, having heard it before.

'I know some of the other jocks here fancy her rotten, and it was the same story in Sydney,' Florian told Luke crudely, genuinely unaware of the variety of reactions he was eliciting. 'Oh, I suppose she's not so bad really, but I honestly don't get it.'

'Florian, how can you be so rude?' Nicky scolded him as if he were a misbehaving son. 'Not to mention tactless. I'm ashamed of you!'

'But I'm fascinated, Nicky,' Luke asserted smoothly. 'If he's really so unique?'

Florian looked pleased, never averse to discussing his own idiosyncrasies which he quite sincerely believed to be endearingly quirky.

'I am unique. But I suppose I'm prejudiced by my first sight of her, a passion-killer if ever there was one. I still see you like that, Maria. Straw boater and a pony-tail, that hideous school uniform hitched up around your thighs so you could show off your legs—God knows why you wanted to when they were covered in hockey bruises, clunky leather lace-ups and ankle socks covered in red dust!' Florian stopped his theatrically narrow-eyed scrutiny of Maria and grinned at Luke, who must have been telling the truth because he was all attention, no less than riveted. 'Do you wonder?

She'd caught two buses across Johannesburg and then walked the last couple of miles to come and find me.'

'To find out how it was done,' Maria corrected him automatically.

'To find out how it worked,' Florian conceded graciously, but Luke was still the audience he was trying to impress. 'The high school I was at was among the first to have a tiny in-school radio station, news, views, interviews and a touch of music, and consequently we'd attracted quite a bit of somewhat condescending attention from *real* stations around town. Maria was absolutely determined that her school wasn't going to be left behind. I suppose you could say we sort of adopted each other, as neither of us had any real brothers and sisters. We've been together ever since, off and on, helping each other out. She even introduced me to my wife, but she knows she didn't exactly do either me or Rachel a favour that time.'

Maria winced as Luke's fingers tightened their hold on hers painfully. Appalled, she hardly dared look at him, afraid of the contempt she would have to face, because of course he would take Florian's insouciant words as confirmation of everything he believed of her.

When she did look at him, she was shocked. Luke accepted it. He accepted that there had never been anything of a romantic or sexual nature between her and Florian.

She began to shake with rage as the lift reached the floor on which her apartment was situated. Luke could believe Florian, whom he disliked——

But he had never believed her.

CHAPTER TEN

MARIA was still shaking violently when she and Luke got out of the lift.

She snatched her hand away from his as if she feared he might contaminate her and stalked ahead of him, not trusting herself to speak until they were inside her apartment.

'You finally believe it, don't you?'

She flung it at him over her shoulder in the hallway before walking into the lounge, choking on the bitterness of knowing that his belief had come too late.

Luke followed her.

'Perhaps you'd better tell me what you were doing, going away for a weekend with a married man,' he suggested quietly.

'I tried to on Friday night,' she reminded him caustically.

'I thought I knew the answer then,' he snapped. 'I've now realised that I don't.'

Because Florian Jones had made him believe that she was innocent of all that he had accused her of. Florian! Luke had never been able to believe *her*. Maria discovered that she was actually jealous of Florian. He had done it so easily too, vanquishing every suspicion of Luke's with a few casual sentences.

'All right!' she relented savagely, her eyes dark in contrast to the pallor of rage. 'Although you shouldn't need to hear it, and you should never have believed what you did in the first place. . . God! For all his ego and vanity, even Florian has never for a moment imagined that I felt any sort of lust or love for him, although he also has no idea just how selfish and immature I do find him outside a broadcasting studio. As he said, I introduced him to Rachel. She was an old school friend, although we were out of school by then. She comes from a very strict family, and only the actual shotgun was missing when she was pregnant within weeks of meeting Flo. I think he might have resisted the pressure her father was putting on him and taken whatever consequences there might have been, but for the prospect of fatherhood. He'll try anything once, and a baby was a novelty. Even now, in his own way, he's proud of Joni. The baby on the way was all that the marriage had going for it, and even then, if Rachel wasn't around, he had a roving eye, and sometimes more than an eye, although at that stage he was technically faithful, I think. I felt guilty—I seem to do that a lot, like when I couldn't be with my parents when my father was dying, even when I know at an intellectual level that I don't need to. It's an emotional thing. . .

'I felt guilty enough to want to help the marriage succeed because I'd introduced them and hadn't thought to warn Rachel, mainly because I didn't find him attractive myself and he'd never come across as the great seducer with me, and I knew that if it didn't work, it would turn out to be a lifelong trap for her. I was naïve enough to think it had a remote chance. I knew she was unhappy about his going away for a whole weekend when she was too sick to accompany him. She was afraid, and so was I. I knew what the atmosphere at stadium events can be like, the way some people discard their inhibitions and normal standards of behaviour. . . Oh, Rachel and I were both naïve when we decided that I should go with him. If he'd met someone and wanted to be unfaithful, he would have found an opportunity and I couldn't have stopped him. Later on, he *was* unfaithful, but not that weekend. So all that was really achieved then was Rachel's temporary peace of mind at a time when she wasn't well. She knew I'd never been interested in Florian. He knows that too. What about you, Luke?'

'I needed to be told,' he conceded drily, facing her across the coffee-table.

'You didn't ask, you didn't want to be told until Florian convinced you that there'd never been anything between us. Florian Jones, Luke! You don't even like him and you believed him, when you've never believed me!' Maria couldn't contain her anguished resentment. 'You bastard! Oh, you bastard!'

'The man is too self-centred to lie for anyone else's sake, and he had nothing to gain by lying for his own.'

'Amazing!' she congratulated him mockingly. 'Because you're dead right about him. You hardly know him, but you can see him that clearly, understand what he's about—and yet you've never understood a thing about me, and we've been together, sharing a bed and our weekends, for weeks now!'

A harshly reluctant sigh shook Luke.

'No excuses here, Maria,' he allowed tautly, and paused a moment before yielding to angry resentment. 'Except that you were right when you once accused me of having a personal prejudice. I arrived in South Africa still stunned by the shock of hearing what my father had had to tell me, half expecting to find marriages being destroyed by outside parties everywhere I looked! But damn it to hell, I've never been able to see clearly or think straight where you're concerned—certainly not since you came to Taipei, and maybe not even six years ago either. I think perhaps that I actually needed to be able to think the worst of you, however personally unpalatable that worst was to me, as some sort of a defence, so that I

could despise you even if it meant despising myself as
well. That way I could feel justified in keeping something back, in not handing myself over to your power
completely—because there was just too much feeling
involved. I couldn't risk believing in you. I didn't *want*
to believe in you.'

'And now, when it's over, Florian has made you
realise that you could quite safely have done so. Is that
ironical, or what?' Maria taunted bitterly, and managed
a falsely consoling smile. 'At least you won't have to
go on feeling ashamed of me in retrospect, Luke, even
if that aspect of it did mar our affair for you. I suppose
that's why you don't seem to mind Nicky and Florian
knowing about it after all now.'

'I was expecting you to deny it when Jones guessed,'
Luke retorted.

'You expected too much of me, then! You had no
right to be ashamed of me, and I knew that all along,
remember, even if you've only just discovered it, so I
didn't see why I should pander to your wish to keep
our affair a secret,' she confessed defiantly. 'As far as
I'm concerned, the whole world could have known
about it.'

'It was never you I was ashamed of, Maria, and as
for keeping our affair secret, I didn't care one way or
the other,' Luke asserted impatiently. 'All that came
from your side——'

'Then why could we never go out together to places
where we might be seen and recognised after we
became lovers?' she demanded scornfully. 'I embar-
rassed you. You didn't want people to know
about us——'

'No, you were the one, darling,' he cut in, irritably
derisive. 'You were ashamed of our relationship. A sex
slave, didn't you once call yourself? Every weekend
there was some little reference to the danger of some-

one realising what was going on, and last Tuesday night too, when I had to come and see for myself if you were all right because the first reports of the earthquake were so horrifying. It may surprise you to know that I could see things from your point of view there. I'd have hated to be in your position, a purely physical attraction outweighing personal antipathy, so I just went along with your wishes. There were even times when I sympathised with you.'

'Oh, come on, Luke!' Maria snapped scathingly. 'I got the idea from you in the first place, from your attitude. Even that very first night, at that party at the Estwicks' place, you were wishing we lived in the days when a man could keep his mistress hidden away.'

'Later I told you I'd been overreacting,' Luke reminded her tightly. 'But I admit that I've said a lot of things in the deliberate hope of hurting or humiliating you, and that was one of them.'

'Punishing me,' she inserted flatly.

'I was driven by the disillusionment of six years ago,' he acknowledged, hard-faced.

'Because you thought I was having an affair with Florian.'

'Until Zimbabwe, I thought I could deal with that. You were so young, at an age to want to experiment and to find a DJ a glamorous figure, that I imagined it was superficial enough to have a time limit on it. I wasn't even sure how far things had gone between you at that stage. Another possibility, also in view of your youth, was that you'd been seduced by the idea of flouting convention by involving yourself with a married man. Youth is sometimes foolish, and rebellion for rebellion's sake seems exciting. I was still debating between taking you away from him, waiting for it to end anyway, or doing nothing at all—the last because I knew that if your reaction to me was purely physical,

I could have you. . .but probably damage you emotionally.'

'Destroy me.' It emerged bleakly. In the end, he had done just that.

'Yes.' A shadow seemed to pass over Luke's face. 'As I say, it was something I was handling. Then the two of you pitched up together in Zimbabwe, and it shocked me into facing realities. To me it meant that your involvement with Jones went deeper than the superficial thing I'd been imagining. Working from my assumption that there was something between the two of you anyway, it seemed obvious that you'd decided to take it much further.'

'So you got me fired from my job,' Maria supplied dully.

'I've never been proud of the way I did that,' Luke said simply. 'You were one of several people who were probably going to be let go on my recommendation as part of a rationalisation programme, but the manner in which I caused it to happen. . . It was the one time in my life I've gone to pieces—lost my mind, I suppose. That was the effect you had on me. I was fundamentally hurt and hitting back. I couldn't bear to see you again. I told myself it was because you disgusted me, but really I was afraid of what I might do and say. Partly it was pride; I couldn't countenance exposing all that I was feeling; but—and I know this doesn't mitigate anything, but perhaps it balances the self-interest, self-protection or whatever it was—even then I was also still afraid of succumbing to the temptation to use the power I sensed I could have over you, and the use would have been abuse.'

'And hasn't it been abuse now, six years later?' Maria prompted resentfully.

'Oh, yes, I know it has, and I don't expect you to spare me, Maria,' Luke conceded sardonically. 'Hell was not having you; having you was equally hell, but a sweeter kind. No excuses, as I've said, and the only explanation I can offer is that I thought you loved Jones. If I'd known you didn't, I'd have tried a different way. . . It doesn't matter now, though. It's over. If you'll excuse me, I'll start telephoning and find out if any of the Hong Kong-bound flights can accommodate me tonight.'

He was turning away from her to go to the telephone. Maria remained motionless, finally beginning to piece the fragments of confession together, assembling a picture of frustration she hardly dared believe she understood.

'What made you suddenly decide it was over?' she asked unevenly. 'On Friday night, Luke?'

He faced her again, his smile a travesty.

'If you remember, *you* had told me it was over and I was. . .persuading you that it wasn't,' he reminded her unwillingly. 'Then suddenly I just couldn't take it any longer—the knowledge that the only effect I had on you was sexual, the only way I could influence you was physically, whereas you loved Jones, as I thought; your relationship with him was emotional. . . Of course, as I now know, that doesn't apply, but the rest still stands. It isn't—it wasn't enough. I want. . .wanted it all or, in the end, I found I wanted nothing, although I'd originally thought I could be satisfied with *something*.'

'Luke——' Shaken, desperately needing to know the cause of such possessiveness, Maria lifted a hand and then let it fall helplessly.

'Additionally, you'd recently started being kind, or tender,' Luke resumed disgustedly, rejection suddenly blazing in his eyes. 'I couldn't bear it, that tenderness that came across so like loving. It mocked me, but at the same time I knew I was in danger of surrendering to it, that damned semblance of what I wanted—I was being weakened by it, seduced into yielding to your power over me, and it's so much more comprehensive than my one-dimensional influence on you. I didn't want to have to face up to how completely. . . I am yours—— And damn it, I've told you I don't expect you to spare me, but I don't have to do this. I don't have to stand here baring my soul in order to make you feel better and less of a victim! I can walk away.'

Acting on it, he turned away again, and Maria went after him, knocking her shin against the coffee-table in her haste. She caught up with him beside the telephone.

'Luke, wait!' The entreaty was breathless and she hesitated, trying to shape words with which to express the single, vital question suddenly hammering away at her mind. 'Please. . .help me. I need you to tell me, to explain——'

'I'm sorry, I'd like to help you, but I just can't,' Luke cut ruthlessly into her stammering plea. 'You'll get over it. You're resilient and intelligent enough to be able to see it for what it was. Right now I'm far more in need of help than you, so I can't afford to consider your needs.'

'Then let me,' she urged agitatedly, touching his bare forearm with gentle fingers. 'Luke. . . Oh, I'm not sure! But maybe I can. Can't you. . .? Can't we——?'

Luke had tensed as she touched him, and after a few seconds he flung her hand off, the violence of the gesture silencing her abruptly.

'Don't do that, Maria! I don't want your kindness. How many times do I have to tell you I can't stand it?' he demanded stormily. 'I can't bear it when you touch me like that!'

Maria had been feeling more vulnerable than she had ever done in her life, but now she lost her temper.

'I'm not being kind when I touch you like that, you

bastard! You don't deserve kindness!' It was tempestuously emphatic.

'Then——'

'I'm being *loving*,' she added the truth passionately.
'You don't deserve that either, damn you, but there it
is. I can't help it. . . Oh, Luke, what's wrong?'

Emotion had darkened his eyes almost to black,
shocking her, but otherwise he kept his expression
rigidly controlled.

'Are you serious?' he asked tautly.

'I suppose you need Florian Jones to convince you
of this as well?' she snapped with furious derision.

'How, Maria?' Ignoring the mockery, Luke's
demand was quietly intense. 'When you've been so
resentful of what was between us—so ashamed of it?
Because you *were* the one who kept going on about the
need to keep it secret. You said you didn't want your
friends and colleagues here knowing about us.'

Maria's anger abated as she realised how much the
answer meant to him.

'I said that to. . .to get back at you, because I
thought you were ashamed of it,' she admitted, beginning to feel slightly guilty. 'It was petty, I know. All
the other times were just a way of reminding myself of
the realities and provoking you at the same time. I was
ashamed of myself, you see. I hated myself for letting
you control my life when you despised me.'

'You hated me as well,' he reminded her warily.

But he was lifting a hand, sliding it beneath the
satiny brightness of her curls, long fingers spreading
and his thumb brushing gently across her cheek. Unaccustomed to such tenderness from this man who had so
rarely shown her anything but contempt and passion,
Maria found herself beginning to tremble, while a hot,
smarting sensation afflicted her eyes and emotion tightened her throat.

'For a long time I thought I did,' she confided softly. 'I kept trying to find all sorts of reasons for doing so. The first time we made love, I started out believing I hated you, but when we. . .by the end I knew I didn't really, and that I loved you. Then for a while I tried loving and hating you all at once, but it didn't work. I couldn't. The love was too much. . . I haven't been able to make myself believe I hate you for some time now, Luke.'

'Ah, God, Maria!' Luke breathed achingly.

She lifted a hand to his, her fingers curving lovingly over the back of his wrist.

'Only it was never really hatred,' she went on shakily. 'I was always frightened of the way I felt, I think because I knew without really understanding it that you could. . .you could own me, Luke. I feared that, but I must always have wanted it too, because when you had me dismissed from that job—— Oh, I hated that, I hated not being able to see you any more, but I thought it was you I hated. I found all sorts of reasons for it, like not being there when my father died. I never understood until I came to Taipei and we met again, when I started to realise why I'd always reacted so strongly to you. At first, when I did, I thought it was purely a physical dependence I'd been afraid of, because I was so slow to understand. It was even worse when I realised that it was more than that. I think I've always loved you, Luke.'

His thumb continued to stroke back and forth over her cheek as he regarded her sombrely.

'You're right, Maria, I don't deserve——'

'Luke!' she broke in urgently, suddenly shaking so badly she could hardly stand. 'Please! I need to know, I need you to tell me if—— All the things you've told me, everything you've felt and wanted. Was it just

possessiveness, wanting it all, all of me, or. . .? Please
tell me!'

'Oh, my God, weren't you sure when you——?'
Luke broke off without completing the shocked question, the appalled look in his eyes gradually giving way
to contrition as he stared at her. 'Then you're braver
than I am, my darling. I love you, Maria. I've always
loved you, from when I first saw you in South Africa,
and without even knowing a thing about you, since you
could never bring yourself to utter a word when I was
around. I never doubted what I was feeling, but I was
shocked when it didn't fade over the years, and I went
through phases of trying to convince myself that it was
some sort of obsession, a perverse desire for the one
woman I believed I could never have—or not in the
way I wanted you, loving me as well as wanting me.'

He sounded so rueful that her heart clenched, and
she lowered her hand, sliding both arms loosely about
him.

'Oh, Luke——' she began, but she couldn't continue, choking on emotion.

'What can I say, Maria?' he asked, his features
tightening as he saw the tears standing in her eyes. 'I
thought you loved Jones—that's why I've treated you
as I have. You must have realised that I resented him.'

'I thought it was just sexual jealousy,' she
acknowledged.

'No, I think I've got my priorities right,' Luke told
her, lifting his other hand to her head. 'You could have
had a hundred casual affairs, and I'd have adjusted to
them somehow and tried to make you fall in love with
me, but the thought that you'd loved someone else and
still loved him, because it seemed to have gone on over
the years, periodically resumed. . . Ah, God!'

He fell silent, but his face was shadowed by the
memory of a very personal anguish, and Maria could

be grateful for the merciful ignorance that had carried her through those same six years in which he had been so haunted.

'If I'd known why it mattered so much to you I'd have tried harder to make you accept the truth,' she said, yielding to her own regrets for a moment. 'I wish I'd known, Luke.'

'And if I had known, even just that you were free to love me if I could persuade you to, I wouldn't have been so——' Breaking off, Luke was once again silent for several seconds. 'But I began this without any hope whatsoever of winning the one thing I wanted above all others because I thought it was already given, and what I took in compensation merely made me want it more and resent its absence, because I kept loving you more and more. God! When I think that every time I rejected your tenderness, it was your love I was reject-ing——'

'It doesn't matter any more, Luke,' Maria stopped him gently. 'We can make it up to each other now, can't we?'

'Yes.' He smiled suddenly, and she caught her breath.

'We love each other,' she realised anew, wonder in her voice.

'So what now?' he asked with a slight uneven laugh.

'We have a future,' she stated confidently.

'Yes.'

Luke's hands were cradling her head and he was kissing her all over her face with an adoring tenderness she would never have dreamed was possible. For a short time she stood still and silent, scarcely breathing as she revelled in the novelty of his tenderness, but presently her body started stirring in response to the warmth of his mouth, a new sweetness to her desire.

'Luke,' she whispered yearningly, moving closer to him. 'My darling?'

'I'm not sure how long I can continue this way right now,' he muttered shakily. 'You see, I want to make love to you and be able to tell you I love you and hear you say you love me while it's happening.'

'I was thinking I'd like exactly the same thing,' she confessed, giving him a radiant smile. 'And there'll be other times. . .'

There would be times for tenderness, and one such time came later, in the aftermath of passion enriched by the knowledge of love, a bonus as they lay touching each other languidly and lovingly, luxuriating in the freedom of being able to express their feelings in this alternative way, confidently but without urgency.

'One thing disappoints me,' Maria mentioned mischievously against Luke's shoulder.

'What?'

'Back there in the lift earlier you didn't instantly and gallantly leap to my defence and punch Florian on the nose when he was carrying on about how undesirable I am!'

Luke laughed, the movement shaking her gently. 'I was too riveted by what I was learning, but I'll do it next time I see him, if you insist, only. . . I never thought the day would come when I'd feel sorry for the man, but I do. If he's never caught his breath at the sight of your crooked smile, or felt his heart lurch with love at the sound of your voice, or watched you walk across a room and wanted you and finally found out that you return his feelings, then he's a poor man and I'm the richest man in the world. Maria?'

'Yes?'

'I want more than just weekends.' His hand smoothed her curls away from her face.

'Me too,' she murmured happily.

'I want to marry you,' he went on.

'I was beginning to think I might have to be the one to raise the question,' she returned demurely.

'No, the next question is yours.'

'A family?'

'If you want one, I'd love it, but I was thinking of more immediate practical considerations.'

Luke had tensed very slightly, and Maria smiled.

'Oh, Luke, a radio station is only a radio station, and there are plenty all around the world, but there's only one Luke Scott.' She laughed as she felt him relax. 'Didn't you know, you fool? Of course, there's the question of my present contract, but I feel sure I can bribe the boss into helping me get out of it without too much hassle.'

'That will depend on what you've got to offer him,' Luke responded, wickedly challenging.

'I'll show you in a little while, my darling—as if you don't already have a very good idea!' laughed Maria.

'We'll work something out,' he promised her.

Their eyes met, sheer delight in each other in both pairs, and then Luke was kissing her on the mouth with so much loving tenderness that she couldn't speak for quite a while.

There would be other practical problems for them to discuss later, she knew, but she was confident that she and Luke would solve them all.

Together, they couldn't fail.

Next Month's Romances

Each month you can choose from a wide variety of romance with Mills & Boon. Below are the new titles to look out for next month, why not ask either Mills & Boon Reader Service or your Newsagent to reserve you a copy of the titles you want to buy — just tick the titles you would like and either post to Reader Service or take it to any Newsagent and ask them to order your books.

Please save me the following titles:		Please tick	√
BABY MAKES THREE	Emma Goldrick		
BETH AND THE BARBARIAN	Miranda Lee		
GRACIOUS LADY	Carole Mortimer		
THE HAWK AND THE LAMB	Susan Napier		
VIKING MAGIC	Angela Wells		
DECEPTIVE PASSION	Sophie Weston		
LOVE ON LOAN	Natalie Fox		
EDGE OF WILDNESS	Christine Greig		
LEARNING TO LOVE	Rosemary Hammond		
PASSIONATE ADVENTURE	Karen van der Zee		
THE BECKONING FLAME	Jessica Hart		
TOO SCARED TO LOVE	Cathy Williams		
NO GOING BACK	Stephanie Howard		
PORTRAIT OF CLEO	Joanna Mansell		
BAY OF RAINBOWS	Dana James		
A WARNING OF MAGIC	Kate Kingston		

If you would like to order these books in addition to your regular subscription from Mills & Boon Reader Service please send £1.70 per title to: Mills & Boon Reader Service, Freepost, P.O. Box 236, Croydon, Surrey, CR9 9EL, quote your Subscriber No:............................ (If applicable) and complete the name and address details below. Alternatively, these books are available from many local Newsagents including W.H.Smith, J.Menzies, Martins and other paperback stockists from 9th April 1993.

Name:...

Address:..

....Post Code:..........................

To Retailer: If you would like to stock M&B books please contact your regular book/magazine wholesaler for details.

You may be mailed with offers from other reputable companies as a result of this application.
If you would rather not take advantage of these opportunities please tick box ☐

Another Face . . .
Another Identity . . .
Another Chance . . .

When her teenage love turns to hate, Geraldine Frances vows to even the score. After arranging her own "death", she embarks on a dramatic transformation emerging as *Silver*, a hauntingly beautiful and mysterious woman few men would be able to resist.

With a new face and a new identity, she is now ready to destroy the man responsible for her tragic past.

Silver – a life ruled by one all-consuming passion, is Penny Jordan at her very best.

WORLDWIDE

An irresistible offer
from Mills & Boon

Here's a personal invitation from Mills & Boon Reader Service, to become a regular reader of Romances. To welcome you, we'd like you to have 4 books, a CUDDLY TEDDY and a special MYSTERY GIFT absolute!y FREE.

Then you could look forward each month to receiving 6 brand new Romances, delivered to your door, postage and packing free! Plus our free Newsletter featuring author news, competitions, special offers and much more.

This invitation comes with no strings attached. You may cancel or suspend your subscription at any time, and still keep your free books and gifts.

It's so easy. Send no money now. Simply fill in the coupon below and post it to -
Reader Service, FREEPOST, PO Box 236, Croydon, Surrey CR9 9EL.

`NO STAMP REQUIRED`

Free Books Coupon

Yes! Please rush me 4 free Romances and 2 free gifts! Please also reserve me a Reader Service subscription. If I decide to subscribe I can look forward to receiving 6 brand new Romances each month for just £10.20, postage and packing free. If I choose not to subscribe I shall write to you within 10 days - I can keep the books and gifts whatever I decide. I may cancel or suspend my subscription at any time. I am over 18 years of age.

Ms/Mrs/Miss/Mr_____ EP31R

Address _____

_____

Postcode_____ Signature _____

mps MAILING PREFERENCE SERVICE